FORESTRY IN CRISIS

The Battle for the Hills

STEVE TOMPKINS

CHRISTOPHER HELM
London

© 1989 Steve Tompkins

Photographs by Steve Moore, Derek Ratcliffe, RSPB/C. Palmar, Steve Tompkins

Christopher Helm (Publishers) Ltd, Imperial House,
21–25 North Street, Bromley, Kent, BR1 1SD

ISBN 0-7470-3206-8

Typeset by Florencetype Ltd, Kewstoke, Avon
Printed and bound in Great Britain by Biddles Ltd, Guildford and Kings Lynn

Contents

Acknowledgements

My thanks to everyone I met along the way,
for all your help and encouragement. I am grateful to
Derek Ratcliffe for reading the book and making invaluable
comments. My thanks also to Elaine Fisher for all of the
typing and re-typing.
I greatly appreciate being able to list, in Table 8.2,
a selection of Scottish landowners from John McEwen's excellent
book *Who Owns Scotland*, published by Polygon (1981).

The photographs originate as follows –

RSPB/C. Palmar 3.6
Steve Moore 3.4, 3.5
Derek Ratcliffe 3.1, 12.7
Steve Tompkins 3.2, 3.3, 5.2, 5.3, 8.3, 9.1,
9.2, 10.2, 10.3, 10.5, 10.6

Figures

Tables

Abbreviations

AONB	Area of Outstanding Natural Beauty
BWGS	Broadleaved Woodland Grant Scheme
CCS	Countryside Commission for Scotland
CLA	Country Landowners Association
CTT	Capital Transfer Tax
DAFS	Department of Agriculture and Fisheries Scotland
EFG	Economic Forestry Group
F&BT	Forestry and British Timber Magazine
FC	Forestry Commission
FCGB	Forestry Committee Great Britain
FGS	Forestry Grant Scheme
FICGB	Forestry Industry Committee Great Britain
FWS	Farm Woodland Scheme
ICF	Institute of Chartered Foresters
NCC	Nature Conservancy Council
NSA	National Scenic Area
RAC	Regional Advisory Committee
RSPB	Royal Society for the Protection of Birds
SSSI	Site of Special Scientific Interest
SWOA(C)	Scottish Woodland Owners Association (Commercial)
SWT	Scottish Wildlife Trust
TGO	Timber Growers Organisation
TGS	Timber Growers Scotland
TGUK	Timber Growers United Kingdom
WGS	Woodland Grant Scheme
WWF	World Wide Fund for Nature

Foreword

Once upon a time Britain had little or no interest in forestry, it only had forestry interests. They got their own way and the public at large could not see the woods for the trees.

But then the trees began to disappear, like the hedgerows before them. At first we blamed Dutch elm disease, until it dawned upon us as a nation that the woodman too was not sparing the tree. We began to agitate. 'Plant a tree in '73', we chorused. But we should have gone on: plant some more in '74, and every year thereafter. Because in the last forty years, in many parts of the country, half the broadleaved woodland has disappeared.

That had to stop. A landscape without trees is about as inviting as the surface of the moon. And a world without woods or woodland is a world without food or shelter for wildlife, and without natural pleasures for people. 'Let us go for a walk in the woods', have been welcome words for centuries.

Since the Second World War whole woods and spinneys of oak and ash and beech in Britain have disappeared under the bulldozer or under the plough. If that had been allowed to continue all the most valuable woods outside the nature reserves – all the ones which delight the eye and shelter the wildlife – would have disappeared by the end of the century. The matter was as urgent as that.

Fortunately there has been a rebirth of broadleaved tree planting, encouraged by the Woodland Trust and the National Trust and many more. But, and it is a very big but, there has also been too much planting, as the scandal of greedy tax avoidance has made public, in the wrong places and of the wrong kind. Blanket afforestation – the march of the alien conifer, which sours the ground and darkens the landscape – is no substitute for an intelligent forestry policy.

The virtue of this book is that it uncovers the activities of the forestry lobby, which still gets too much of its own way. It makes plain the absence of any intelligent forestry policy. And it then explains what needs to be done.

This is a policy document, better than any White Paper, and it ought not to be ignored.

Brian Redhead,
President of The Council for National Parks

About the Author

Steve Tompkins is a forestry graduate of Edinburgh University. He joined the Forestry Commission as an assistant district officer and worked in the New Forest and the Lake District. In 1980 he joined one of the main private forestry companies as an acquisitions manager and was responsible for the survey and valuation of land and forests throughout northern England and south Scotland. Since 1986 he has worked as forestry officer for the Peak District National Park. He wrote *The Theft of the Hills – Afforestation in Scotland* for the Ramblers Association and the World Wildlife Fund, which was published in August 1986.

The views expressed are entirely the personal ones of the author, and not those of any employer, past or present.

Introduction – The Turning Point

It was a rare and perfect summer's evening. A burn flowed through the darkening glen, and the hills lay folded around it, slumbering in the calm, warm air. Drawn by the magnetism of the hilltop above, I set off in my shirtsleeves, every footstep spilling pollen from the purple heather. From the summit the hills stretched off into the sunset, and I watched a peregrine falcon scull across the moor with clipped wingbeats, a dark head turned towards me.

Looking down I could see the stark outline of the road which had been bulldozed across the hills. The top of the road cut sharply into the soil and rock leaving an eroding scar. The bottom edge was a steep embankment of bare, loose stone. The track rose up to nearly 1,700 ft above sea-level in a sharp, hairpin bend, where my company car was parked with my jacket hanging in the back. I was there on business. It was my job to see that the maximum area of these beautiful hills was fenced, ploughed, drained and planted with conifers.

I had driven past the young Forestry Commission plantations, which marched over the tops of the hill at 1,600 ft, and now the private forestry company for which I worked was bent on extending the forest into the silent heart of the hills. The glen also contained a ruined pele-tower whose battlements had protected a farmer from raiders hundreds of years ago. It seemed an incongruous feature in this secluded setting, but now a new onslaught was looming. In a few months the quiet evolution of a centuries old system of sheep farming would be shattered by subsidised conifer afforestation, and the hills would be completely transformed.

That evening was a turning point and my work was never the same again, for I realised that the balance of land-use in the hills has tilted too far. Forestry is an ancient and reputable profession, but the aberrations of ill-conceived policies have drawn a blanket of conifers across vast areas of hill and moor, often onto the poorest ground for tree growth. But while conifer afforestation in the uplands has flourished for over 40 years, many of the lowland, broadleaved woodlands that are so important for landscape and wildlife, have been neglected, replaced with conifers, or cleared for agriculture. We need to be clear why this has happened and, having established why, to then build a new approach to forestry in Britain.

Part One

Blanket Afforestation
The Threat to the Uplands

= 1 =

The Upland Heritage

From the crumbling, sandstone towers of Suilven, to the shattered, volcanic fragments of Tryfan, and the eroded gritstone of Kinder Scout, there is a journey of discovery and enjoyment for anyone who ventures into Britain's upland countryside. The exhilarating diversity of the hills and moors can embrace wildness and grandeur, or warmth and intimacy, and changes with the seasons, the days and the passing weather. The variety of landscapes ranges from the shapely peaks at the head of Wastwater in the Lake District, to the quiet, grassy hills that roll across the border between England and Scotland.

The stresses and strains imposed by intensive agriculture are clearly evident in the suffering, lowland countryside, where hedgerows and meadows have been steadily destroyed. In the hills, the progress of modern farming has often been restrained by the rugged terrain and the harsh climate, so that the intrusion of man and his activities may be less apparent. There is an atmosphere of freedom and unspoilt nature that can still be savoured in the uplands, providing a haven for the inhabitants of a densely populated group of islands. Whether they provide the joy of a climber reaching the summit, a family picnic by the roadside, or pictures for an office calendar, the hills and moors are a source of inspiration to all of us.

Such is the variety of Britain's countryside that it is difficult to define the uplands precisely, but there are some 15–17 million acres (6–7 million ha) of hills, moors and rough grazing. A good, general definition of upland countryside in England and Wales is provided by land that is more than 800 ft (240 m) above sea-level. Such high ground is a relatively scarce resource in England, where just 13 per cent of land exceeds that elevation, compared to 39 per cent of Wales. The outstanding landscapes of the English and Welsh uplands are recognised by the designation of the National Parks and Areas of Outstanding Natural Beauty (AONBs) shown in Figure 1.1. About 60 per cent of English uplands, and 30 per cent of those in Wales are designated in these ways.

In Scotland's spectacular countryside, land with an upland character can be found down to sea-level, and it is estimated that

Figure 1.1 *The upland heritage of England and Wales: left, land over 800' a.s.l.; right, National Parks and AONBs*

there are 10.9 million acres (4.4 million ha), occupying about 55 per cent of the total land area. Scotland has no National Parks, but 40 National Scenic Areas (NSAs) have been designated, covering 13 per cent of the total land surface (Figure 1.2).

Britain's uplands are also an extremely valuable nature conservation resource, one of their most important and unique habitats being blanket bog. Located in the north and west of Britain the bogs are exposed to winds and rain carried across 2,500 miles of ocean by the North Atlantic westerlies, and two days in every three have significant rainfalls over much of the Scottish highlands. In such a cool, wet climate the remains of plants and mosses do not decompose fully and begin to accumulate as peat. Over the last 4,000–7,000 years this peat has gradually laid an organic mantle of blanket bog over great tracts of the uplands. Despite its unflattering name, blanket bog on such a scale is a world rarity and Britain boasts at least 10 per cent of the world's total area. Elsewhere, it is only found in restricted locations with a suitable climate including Patagonia, New Zealand, Alaska and Iceland (Figure 1.3). The moors of Caithness and Sutherland in the far north of Scotland are the greatest continuous blanket bog in Europe and are unique in world terms.

Despite the restrictions imposed by climate, terrain, difficult communications and poor soils, the uplands have provided a living for farmers and estate owners. Low intensity systems of management have evolved and the land has been used for sheep farming,

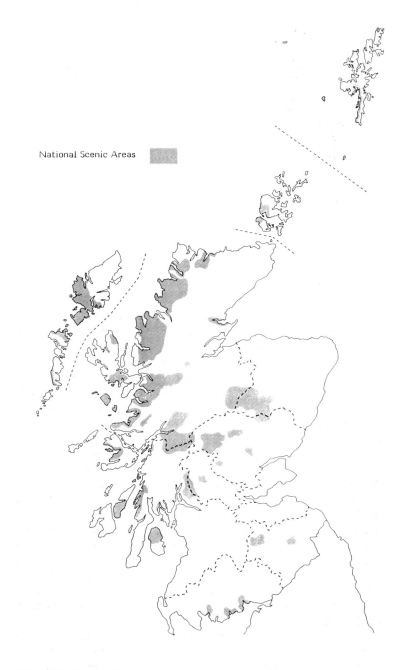

National Scenic Areas

Figure 1.2 *Scotland's National Scenic Areas*

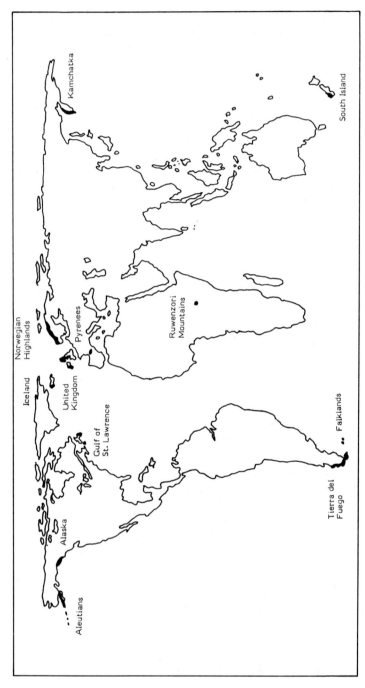

Figure 1.3 *World distribution of blanket bog*

grouse moor, and as a range for red deer. Properly managed, these systems of land-use can sustain an environment that also supports a rich diversity of wildlife. Most upland soils have never been broken by a plough, whole hills are unfenced, and fertilisers, herbicides and pesticides have rarely been used. As a result the upland countryside has a degree of naturalness that is highly valued by conservationists and hill walkers. Although much of Britain's hill land once carried forests of native trees, by Roman times these were cleared from most of upland England and Wales and from Scotland more than 400 years ago. Until recently the pace of change has continued to be slow and the ground vegetation on the hills today is often the same as that which grew under the trees and over the glades of the original forests.

The rich variety of semi-natural vegetation on the hills needs a close examination to be appreciated fully, as it changes across the different soils and slopes of the ground. Streamsides, flushed with nutrients, grow the golden flowers of the yellow mountain saxifrage. On the lower slopes of the hill there might be bog myrtle, heather and purple moor grass, with mat grass on the thinner peats. Bog asphodel and deer sedge survive on the poorest ground, with mountain sedge and least willow amongst the rocks on the summit. Birds such as snipe, redshank and lapwing, and animals like the frog, are all greatly reduced in numbers in the lowlands but can still be found in the hills. The Nature Conservancy Council (NCC) has rightly valued (1986) the uplands as 'the last stronghold of wildlife in Britain'.

The forestry view

Before going further, it is time to hear from the forestry world. Table 1.1 gives a selection of quotes which illustrates forestry attitudes to the uplands, demonstrating that the finer points of wildlife and scenery are sometimes undervalued. Foresters often prefer to denigrate the uplands as a barren, unproductive, bleak, bare wasteland. This transparent campaigning is a device adopted to give themselves permission to afforest as much of the uplands as possible.

Further campaigning by the lobby focuses on the designation of the countryside. The Timber Growers' Organisation (TGO) preferred to be able to carry out its operations without the 'increasing problems stemming from interference in forestry by planning authorities . . .' (*F&BT* May 1972). The TGO also pronounced that: 'We do not condemn the existing National Parks and Areas of Outstanding Natural Beauty but we see no point in extending them'

Table 1.1: *The forestry view of the uplands*

'It is worth reiterating Lord Taylor's valid defences.
Bare uplands – where planting is mainly done on land
which can only bear conifer crops – is normally devoid
of wildlife.'

F&BT February 1972

'It is scandalous that vast tracts of upland Britain lie
barren awaiting productive development.'

F&BT editorial May 1978

'As Leslie Troup, Forestry Commission conservator,
emphasised, there were 10,000 ha of Dartmoor crying
out for afforestation. Environmentalists might react
with horror but we understand Mr Troup's assertion
that such a development would be right "economically,
scenically and ecologically".'

F&BT editorial 1979

'Britain cannot afford the luxury of a countryside
petrified as a free park for the visual delights of ramblers
and "eco-freaks".'

F&BT editorial May 1980

'Crystallising our uplands into parade grounds for the
rucksack brigade . . .'

F&BT editorial November 1980

'Afforesting the hundreds of thousands of hectares of
Britain's wasted, unproductive and unmanaged
woodlands and common land . . .'

F&BT editorial April 1982

'Technical advances have enabled the forester to create
thriving woodlands on quaking peat bogs that were
virtually useless and valueless . . .'

J. Davies (1985)

(*F&BT* July 1979). This view seems to be shared by the Forestry Commission (FC) itself, with one of its spokesmen describing the proposed AONB designation of the Clwydian range of hills in north-west Wales as 'not particularly helpful' (*F&BT* March 1983).

The forestry lobby clearly takes an active campaigning stance in its attitude to the uplands, and its members like to depict themselves as the level-headed practitioners of commercial reality. A favourite tactic is to decry any opposing views as naive and emotional. The aim is to cover as much of the uplands as possible with conifer plantations, contributing, in the Flow Country, to what the NCC has described as the most massive single loss of wildlife habitat in Britain since the Second World War (1986).

Blanket tree-farming

The intensification of agriculture has taken a dreadful toll on wildlife habitats in the lowlands. The NCC (1984) has estimated that 95 per cent of lowland neutral grassland now lacks significant wildlife interest and only 3 per cent is undamaged by modern farming. Nearly 80 per cent of lowland chalk grassland has been lost to arable fields and improvements, 30 per cent of hedges in England and Wales were destroyed by 1974, and 40 per cent of lowland heaths have disappeared under conifer forests, improved fields and building developments.

The wildlife value of the uplands has also been damaged by modern farming practices. Characteristic upland habitats of grassland heath and blanket bog have been affected by agricultural improvements, reclamation, burning and overgrazing, and these factors account for some of the 30 per cent of these habitats that have been lost or significantly damaged during the last 50 years. But the greatest damage in the uplands has been caused by the tree farmers.

The vocabulary of an upland forester draws irresistible comparisons with agriculture. Afforestation of a bare hillside requires fencing, the elimination of wildlife such as hares and deer (regarded as vermin), deep ploughing and drainage, planting, fertilising and weeding. All the techniques of modern agriculture are applied including the aerial application of pesticides to control insect attack. Today's foresters talk of rotations, crops and harvests. Their crops have become steadily more dependent on a single, alien tree species, the Sitka spruce, with lodgepole pine used where the ground is poorest. Tree-breeding programmes are also ensuring that the genetic base of the plants used will steadily decrease.

The harsh growing conditions in the uplands dictate that many tree crops can never be thinned out, and blanket afforestation means that hundreds of acres are all of the same age. Timber harvesting is becoming increasingly mechanised. Highly-expensive sophisticated harvesting and processing machinery can now be used to fell trees, trim their branches, and cut them into lengths, in a clear reminder of the way that a combine would clear a field of wheat. Upland foresters themselves are slow to recognise their true status as tree farmers, and rely on a public image that has more to do with checked shirts and axemanship.

With a shortage of good-quality forestry land, Taylor (1987a) pointed out: 'We do not really want to go on planting trees above the 1,000 ft (300 m) contour, where technically we can plant only the unloved and unlovely Sitka spruce. This is as professionally and emotionally stunting as being forced to grow only oilseed rape. It pays, but there must be more to life than this.'

Rowan (1986) compares forestry with modern farming. He thinks that afforestation 'represents a significant technical achievement, which stands comparison with the great successes in improved agricultural production. The forests are, understandably, very different in character from the woodlands lost in earlier times, in much the same way that modern agriculture differs from, say, mediaeval farming.'

Another forester's view of the nature of some modern tree farming, carried out when less attention was paid to landscape and wildlife, comes from Baguley (1985): 'It is fair to say that foresters mainly looked on planting conifers in the same way as a farmer looks on growing a crop of barley or turnips – namely they were concerned with establishing just another commercial crop, one composed mainly of cellulose.'

The crucial point is that blanket afforestation threatens the uplands in just the way that intensive agriculture has ravaged the lowland countryside, and both activities are massively dependent on public subsidies. The semi-natural vegetation on the hills is itself a truly renewable natural resource that is self-sustaining. The forestry lobby likes to think that upland conifer plantations can be regarded in the same way, but this is totally refuted by Bowers (1983). Blanket afforestation consists of even-aged, conifer monocultures, that are harvested and replanted, like any crop of surplus grain, except that the trees take decades to grow.

— 2 —

The Theft of the Hills

The moving target

The first basic ingredient of recent British forestry policy has always been an obsession with a target area of bare land to be afforested.

During the First World War about 450,000 acres (182,000 ha) of mostly broadleaved woodland were felled. Much of this timber provided the pit props for the coal mines which fuelled the industrial war effort. Concern about strategic timber supplies to meet the needs of future wars lay behind the Forestry Act of 1919. This Act formed the foundations of today's forestry policy and practices. The Forestry Commission was created to oversee the afforestation process, and with the legal status of a government department, it was the first state-controlled production industry. Of course the Act also set a target – 1.8 million acres (0.75 million ha) of new forests. It is interesting to note that over 5 per cent of this area was envisaged as broadleaved planting, compared to the lamentable achievement of less than 1 per cent broadleaves in recent upland afforestation.

The Second World War came all too soon, and the earliest FC plantations can only have been 20 years old. More timber was needed for the war effort and woodlands were felled at the rate of 1,800 acres (730 ha) per week, up to a total of 484,000 acres (196,000 ha). Only 29,000 acres (12,000 ha) of this total were FC forests. As Allied shipping losses continued, concern about a strategic reserve of timber led to a new target being set in 1943. This time, interestingly, it was not a detached committee which set the target, but the men at the top of the FC itself, the Forestry Commissioners. Their report pushed the target for the total afforested area up to 3 million acres (1.2 million ha). A further 2 million acres (0.8 million ha) of 'effective' forest were to be created by restocking existing woodlands.

The strategic justification for forestry continued until 1957 when the Zuckerman Committee finally rejected it, realising that a Third World War was likely to consist of a brief, nuclear exchange. But the committee did not delve too deeply into the rationale underlying afforestation. After 38 years the forestry lobby had grown powerful enough to ensure that afforestation would continue as before, and the justification for it was merely changed to the creation and diversification of employment in rural areas.

The increasingly cosy world of forestry was shocked by the 1972 *Interdepartmental Cost-Benefit Study* by the Treasury. This scathing examination of the basis of state forestry was followed by the change from Estate Duty to Capital Transfer Tax (CTT) which plunged private forestry into crisis. Only intensive lobbying allowed the afforestation industry to survive, with the provision of rural employment as its slim justification. The time was ripe for the lobby to strike back. Its need for new targets was paramount, particularly as the 1917 target had been achieved twice over, and the 1943 targets were about to be passed. In 1977 the FC published *The Wood Production Outlook in Britain: a Review* predictably calling for a massive expansion of up to 4.4 million acres (1.8 million ha) of new planting. This was followed by a report from a group of forestry academics who called for up to another 4.8 million acres (1.9 million ha) of planting (Centre for Agricultural Strategy 1980).

In the wake of this lobbying a ministerial statement in December 1980 announced a forestry policy which was remarkably like the old one, only this time the aim was to reduce imports. Most importantly, however, there was no mention of a total area of plantations that was to be achieved. Instead, afforestation was envisaged as continuing at the existing rate of 50,000–60,000 acres (20,000–25,000 ha) per year. This handed the forestry lobby an open-ended remit to carry on planting, free from the embarrassment of ever having to admit that it had reached a pre-determined, upper limit to the area of plantations. The 1980 policy statement also emphasised that an increasingly important role was to be played by the private sector.

Despite rising criticism of blanket afforestation, and perhaps to comfort the forestry lobby, the open-ended annual target was increased to 75,000 acres (30,000 ha) in March 1986. Astonishingly, a further increase to 81,500 acres (33,000 ha) was announced in 1987. This was despite the fact that the target was clearly being missed in practice with only 57,000 acres (23,000 ha) being planted, on average each year between 1984 and 1986. The forestry lobby makes splendid use of this 'shortfall', for in the world of lobbying and manipulation it helps to have a target which you are not achieving so that you can claim you are hard done by.

The key to understanding forestry policy is that ever since 1919 – whilst targets may have been revised, whilst the balance between state and private forestry may have shifted, whilst tax and grant incentives have varied, and even though the fundamental justifications have been juggled – upland afforestation has continued inexorably. Over the last 60 years an average of nearly 45,000 acres (18,000 ha) have been planted each year.

Why plant trees in the uplands?

The second basic ingredient of British forestry is that the rapid expansion of coniferous plantations has occurred on land where tree growth is least satisfactory – in the uplands. Infertile soils, difficult terrain and the harsh climate are all problems, and wind damage has been found to be the main constraint on forest growth and management in the hills. Fountain Forestry's 1987 brochure on the merits of investment in North America contrasts the availability of 'highly fertile' growing conditions with Britain, where: 'Forestry has been pushed out into the hills and uplands utilising the poorest soils and most exposed sites.' The practice of upland planting has become so ingrained since 1919 that the reasons for it have not often been examined in detail, but new attempts to encourage lowland farmers to plant trees may provoke a closer scrutiny.

Afforestation began in the uplands principally to avoid competition with agriculture, as the production of food was seen to be of key importance, and to minimise conflict with farming landowners. Over the years subsidised agriculture has flourished to the point of excess, and a series of factors have conspired to relegate afforestation firmly into the hills. Timber prices in Britain are set by a world market, dominated by major exporting nations, so that home-grown timber has always been a low-value crop. Simple economics have dictated that afforestation in Britain could only take place on cheap land. It also has to be carried out on a large scale, to reduce unit costs, and the only place where cheap land is held in large units of ownership is in the uplands.

Afforestation throughout Britain

The forestry lobby likes to bombard us with the fact that only 10 per cent of Britain is under trees, both long established woodland and new plantations, which is a lower proportion of tree cover than in most other countries of the European Community. But this is an entirely simplistic view. The expansion of afforestation in Britain has been almost exclusively confined to the uplands. A considerable area of these uplands, especially in Scotland, is not currently considered suitable for planting because it is too high or too steep, so that forest expansion is further restricted to what is known as the sub-montane zone. It is the substantial proportion of this zone that

has already been afforested that is crucial. Just under 20 per cent of
the plantable land in the English uplands, 28 per cent in Wales, and
34 per cent of that in Scotland, has been afforested (Figure 2.1).
These percentages are an excellent match for the proportion of land
in other European countries that is under forest.

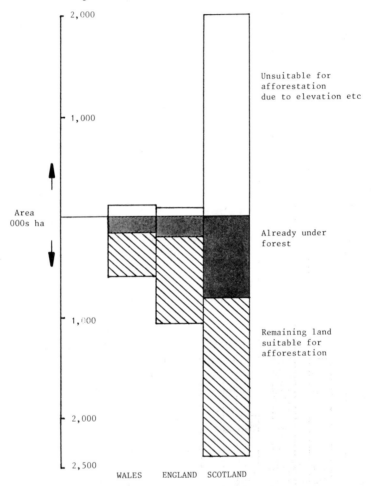

Figure 2.1 *Areas of hill, moor and rough grazing in Wales, England and
Scotland*   Source: NCC 1986

The age structure of Britain's mainly coniferous forests, both
state and private (Figure 2.2), illustrates the pattern of planting
throughout this century. Although the replanting of forests that
were felled during wartime is included, the expansion of the forest

area in recent decades is almost entirely due to the planting of bare land in the uplands. The most striking, and most worrying, aspect of afforestation is the way it has boomed since the Second World War. Since 1945 the area of FC plantations alone has quadrupled from just under half-a-million acres (200,000 ha), to over 2.2 million

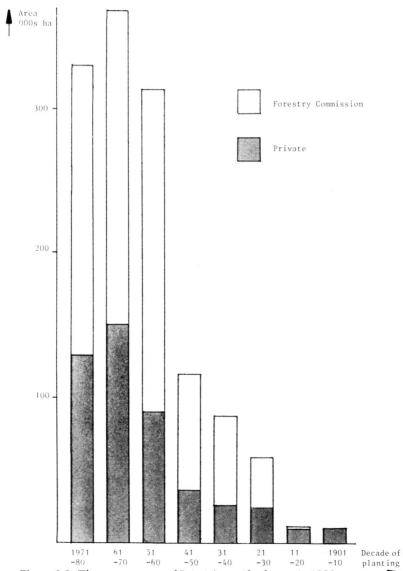

Figure 2.2 *The age structure of Britain's conifer forests in 1980*
Source: Forestry Commission 1987b

acres (0.9 million ha). There has been a headlong rush to afforest the uplands which is reflected in the youth of conifer plantations throughout Britain. One of the most notable findings of the most recent FC census was that 85 per cent of all coniferous forest had been planted since 1940 (FC 1987b).

The continued surge of afforestation, despite the fact that the initial strategic justification has been stripped away, demonstrates the power and influence that the forestry lobby has accumulated. In the ten years between 1976 and 1985 alone, new planting covered another 560,000 acres (227,000 ha) of land, an area almost the size of Cheshire (NCC 1986).

Afforestation in England and Wales

The changing pattern of afforestation in England and Wales can be seen in the age structures of their mainly coniferous forests (Figure 2.3).

In England, afforestation by the FC reached a peak during the 1950s. The vast Kielder Forest spread over the rough grazings of Northumberland and Cumbria at that time, on its way to becoming the largest man-made forest in Europe. Planting by the FC continued into the 1960s at high levels but then started to decline. This setback was largely the result of the spirited public opposition which has always greeted afforestation in England, and was manifested in the 1936 agreement between the FC and the Council for the Protection of Rural England (CPRE) to leave key parts of the central area of the Lake District bare of conifer plantations. The forestry lobby often decries opposition to planting as a recent phenomenon, fed by public ignorance, but 50 years of steady resistance indicates otherwise. Private afforestation in England reached its peak in the 1960s and early 1970s when plantations spread across Northern Cumbria and the Yorkshire Dales. This was a boom period for private forestry and only the CTT crisis of the mid-1970s and growing public concern slowed the expansion.

Afforestation in Wales followed a similar trend to that in England, although private forestry has taken a secondary role, possibly due to the tendency of Welsh plantations to be set on fire, which has a deterrent effect on investors. The pattern of decline is also similar so that: 'One well-known Welsh forester remarked that he considered that large-scale planting in Wales (which means anything over 250 acres), was a thing of the past, so all-embracing had become the objections' (Taylor 1987b).

Despite the rising tide of public opposition, afforestation was able to make a considerable impact on the National Parks of

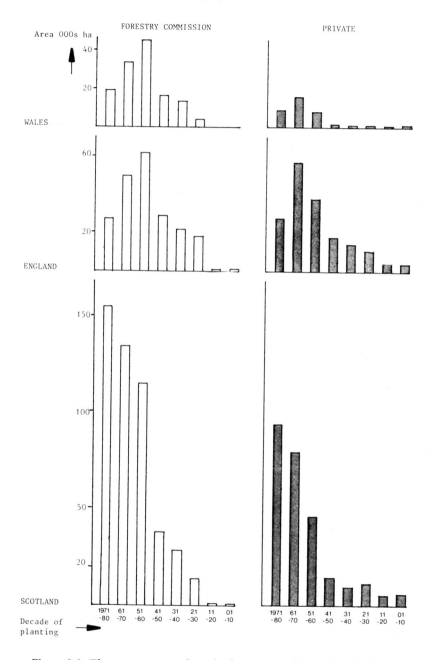

Figure 2.3 *The age structure of conifer forests in Wales, England and Scotland in 1980*   Source: Forestry Commission 1987b

England and Wales. In 1979 alone, the FC increased its ownership in the Parks by 8 per cent through acquisitions in Snowdonia and the Lake District. By 1980 a fifth of the whole of the FC estate in the two countries was in the Parks, covering 427 sq miles (110,660 ha), of which 75 per cent was planted. The FC attaches great importance to these conspicuous holdings and is prepared to go to a great deal of expense to carry out cosmetic modifications to the edges of ugly blocks of conifers, such as at Ennerdale in the Lake District. Maximum publicity is extracted from such exercises, as part of a wider campaign to make the overall expansion of afforestation more palatable.

The culmination of opposition to afforestation in England came with the Secretary of State for the Environment's announcement in 1988. This made it clear that further approval would not normally be given for large-scale conifer planting in the uplands of England. While this must be welcomed, there must be great concern that it will result in increased pressures to afforest more of Wales and Scotland.

Afforestation in Scotland

As public opposition continued unabated in England and Wales, Scotland became the centre of the afforestation industry with a continuous expansion of state and private planting (Figure 2.3). But the industry was not in Scotland because it wanted to be there. At a farming and forestry conference in 1987 an FC spokesman admitted, in an unguarded reply, that afforestation companies were investing in Scotland because it was 'less hassle'.

Between 1975 and 1984 new planting in Scotland went on at an annual rate of close to 50,000 acres (20,000 ha), and resulted in an increase in the total forest area of 21.5 per cent (Mather and Murray 1986). In the year 1985/86 over 91 per cent of all the afforestation in Britain took place in Scotland. The removal of the FC headquarters to Edinburgh in 1975 confirmed afforestation as a mainly Scottish affair, and this is clearly shown in Figure 2.4.

Blanket afforestation

Blanket afforestation is an apt description of the way in which conifer plantations have spread across whole regions of Britain's upland countryside, although the term is regarded as pejorative by the forestry lobby. The dismal process is largely achieved by just 40–60 major afforestation schemes in any year, each covering 250–3,000 acres of land (100–1,200 ha), with some planting

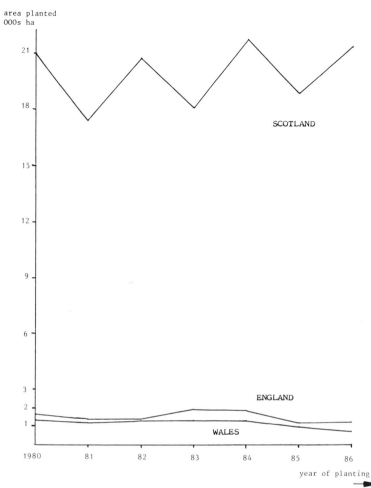

Figure 2.4 *The predominance of afforestation in Scotland 1980 to 1986*
Source: Forestry Commission Annual Reports 1980–87

proposals in the far north of Scotland extending to a colossal 4,500 acres (1,800 ha). Forestry on this scale transforms the relatively intimate nature of Britain's rolling hills and moors. A 250 acre (100 ha) scheme creates a 'doormat' of conifers on a hillside, 500 acres (200 ha) covers a whole hillside from the fields in the valley to the high tops, and a 3,000 acre plantation (1,200 ha) blankets a whole watershed with trees along the sides of an entire valley.

The devastating impact on landscape and wildlife is steadily compounded by the tendency of plantations to link up and cover great tracts of hill land. This subjective impression is confirmed by Mather and Murray (1986) who found that just over 60 per cent of a sample of Scottish forestry schemes shared common boundaries with other forests. Grouping of forests is caused by afforestation companies targeting an area of countryside for expansion, as has happened on Islay and in the Flow Country. Once company representatives become established in an area and known to local landowners, the pace of afforestation starts to accelerate. This 'spread effect' has important implications for the way in which new planting should be planned and controlled, but these are ignored at present. Once afforestation begins in a locality it is also more difficult for objectors to argue against subsequent expansion.

In some parts of the uplands there is very little land that remains unplanted and virtually unbroken blocks of conifer plantations have been created over large areas. Figure 2.5 shows the location of forestry 'blackspots', including the Cheviots with nearly 231 sq miles (60,000 ha) planted, Galloway and Carrick with 309 sq miles (80,000 ha), and Eskdalemuir and Craik with 120 sq miles (31,000 ha).

Fountain Forestry moved in and purchased 151 sq miles (39,000 ha) of the Flow Country in just five years. This brought one third of the area identified by the Royal Society for the Protection of Birds (RSPB) as important for birds under forestry control. The speed at which afforestation can spread is also shown by the development of plantations at Eskdalemuir in south Scotland. The bulk of this area was blanketed with conifers in just six years between 1967 and 1972 when over 23,700 acres (9,600 ha) were planted. Further major acquisitions during the 1980s have extended the plantations even further.

Despite the creation of such vast plantations, forestry interests will pursue the last remnants of unplanted land in a heavily afforested region with vigour. The lower slopes of the massive Scottish mountain, Creag Meagaidh, are the last unplanted hillside in a 20 mile (32 km) stretch of upland countryside and were designated as a Site of Special Scientific Interest (SSSI). But Fountain Forestry and the FC pursued the case for planting this last, open remnant to ministerial level and only the purchase of the site as a nature reserve by the NCC prevented afforestation. Even though the proportion of land under conifer plantations in Dumfries and Galloway rose from 2 to 23 per cent over a 40 year period, the FC did not hesitate to see the potential for a further expansion of 1,350 sq miles (350,000 ha) of plantations there, and in the Borders Region (NCC 1986). Prospects such as these led the president of the National Farmers' Union for Scotland to say: 'There are many areas of Scotland, particularly in Galloway and Argyll, where hill and upland farming has been effectively eliminated and the traditional landscape of bare, rolling hills has been replaced by continuous lines of conifers marching to the horizon and beyond' (*F&BT* November 1979).

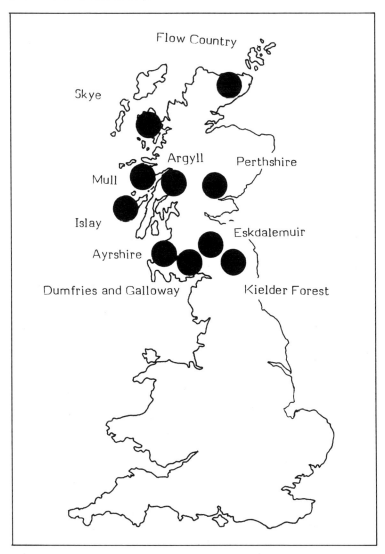

Figure 2.5 *Forestry blackspots*

= 3 =

The Environmental Impact

The value of naturalness

The conservation value of ancient woodlands such as the Caledonian pine forests is closely related to their naturalness, and the way in which man's influence has been low key. More intensive management of natural habitats, for the production of food or timber, is usually associated with a simplification of the structure and diversity of the site, leading to a loss in wildlife value. The NCC (1986) describes a continuum of naturalness ranging from the wholly natural to the completely artificial. So pervasive is man's influence that the former is rare in Britain, but undisturbed vegetation on inaccessible cliff ledges, or coastal habitats are the most likely examples.

Much of Britain's upland countryside of hills, moors and rough grazing can be described as semi-natural. Although it has been modified by cutting, burning and grazing, it may carry ground vegetation that has changed little for hundreds or thousands of years, and can have a correspondingly high value for wildlife. The key features of natural and semi-natural habitats are that they are diverse, fragile, and extremely difficult, if not impossible to recreate. Many such habitats have already become rare in Britain and if examples of considerable size remain, then they are valued accordingly.

Blanket afforestation is a prime example of intensive human management, creating a more artificial habitat, that may be less valuable for wildlife than the semi-natural moors it replaces. Vast acreages of alien conifers have all the uniformity and mass production efficiency of a field of wheat, and the contrast with the ancient Caledonian pine forest could not be more complete. The purpose of modern plantations is to maximise the financial return from the forest. It requires the production of the maximum volume of timber in the shortest possible time.

There is a crucial question, over which a battle for the hills is being fought. How far should the expansion of intensive tree-farming, and the artificial habitats that it creates, be allowed to proceed, before the damage to upland habitats which are

Figure 3.1 *Ancient forest – Caledonian pines at Abernethy Forest in Inverness-shire. Old and young trees, with a lush ground vegetation of juniper, heather, bilberry, cowberry and mosses*

Figure 3.2 *Modern plantation – an impenetrable thicket of Sitka spruce, a conifer introduced from North America, in the Forestry Commission's vast Kielder Forest in Northumberland*

Figure 3.3 *Dark as the night – an unthinned crop of spruce in the Forestry Commission's Kielder Forest. Virtually all the ground flora is eliminated in the dense, dark plantation*

indisputably at the more natural end of the continuum of naturalness becomes unacceptable?

The impact of afforestation

The process of afforestation comes as a shattering intrusion into a semi-natural environment. Unenclosed land is first fenced, itself a violation of open landscapes that are cherished for their atmosphere of freedom. The site may then be ploughed and drained with forestry ploughs that can cut to a depth of 2 to 3 ft (60 to 90 cm). The plough furrows and upturned turves can cover 40 per cent of the ground surface, reducing the semi-natural vegetation to residual ribbons.

The young conifers are planted on the upturned turves just 6 to 8 ft apart (1.8 to 2.4 m), and in ten years or less, their branches converge to create the aptly named 'thicket stage', so that the space between the rows becomes impassable. So dark does the ground under the trees become that all the remaining ground vegetation is exterminated, and not even ferns and mosses can survive.

On better sites the trees can be periodically thinned out, beginning at about 20 years of age, and the continuance of this operation over a 50 or 60 year period can produce a lighter and more open forest. But this is not possible on many of the exposed upland sites which have been the subject of afforestation. So great is the risk of wind damage that such plantations can only be grown for 30–35 years and they can never be thinned, remaining dense and dark for all of their shortened rotations. As Moncrieff (1985) realised, current trends are leading to 'more no-thin and respaced stands which prolong the thicket stage – generally thought to be the least attractive visually and environmentally – to three-quarters of the life of the crop'.

During their short lives such plantations may be fertilised or sprayed with insecticide from the air, before they are clearfelled and replanted with similar crops. Surely there can be no doubt, even in the most enthusiastic forester's mind, that these agricultural, tree crops have less value in both conservation and wider human terms, than ancient woodlands; and that they are no replacement for the conservation value of the semi-natural moorland on which they are planted. The fundamental point is that blanket afforestation causes an ecological transformation, as recognised by Holmes (1979): 'In establishing forests on bare uplands it is hard to imagine a more dramatic change in the ecological conditions including the soil, the flora, the fauna, and not least the introduction of trees for the first time in centuries.'

The words of the NCC (1986) provide a stark summation of the conservation issues: 'When the heaths, grasslands, peatlands or sand dunes that are lost to afforestation have special nature conservation value in their previous state, the forests that replace them, however good they may become for wildlife, are not, and never can be, an adequate substitute.'

The loss of moorlands and peat bogs

It is often claimed by foresters that in the uplands they are planting and improving very widespread and ordinary habitats which are poor in every way – in flora and fauna, as well as in agricultural productivity. They have pointed to the extent and uniformity of large areas of mat grass, flying bent, sheep fescue, bracken, deer sedge, heather and bilberry, and other hill vegetation. Yet they fail to acknowledge that their activities have already substantially reduced the total area of many of these moorland communities, to the point that, in many heavily afforested districts there is now serious concern about how much of these types is eventually going to remain. Many of these characteristic British upland vegetation types either have a very restricted distribution in continental Europe, or do not occur there at all.

The world rarity of blanket bog, and the unique nature of the Flow Country in northern Scotland have been outlined in Chapter 1. The flows have been described by the International Mire Conservation Group as the largest and finest example of a landscape which is thousands of years old (1986). The Group rated the flows as one of the world's outstanding natural features, comparing it in importance to the African Serengeti or the South American rainforests. Man's influence on the flows has been very limited and they would probably look much the same now, if man had never appeared on the scene. The wettest surfaces of the peat in parts of Caithness have not carried trees since the last ice age, and ancient woodlands would only have occupied the better soils and more sheltered locations of the valleys.

Climbing to one of the isolated areas of higher ground in the flows can provide a view across 40 miles (64 km) of country. There is a wild character to the land, resembling as it does, a southern outlier of the Arctic tundra. The surface of the peat is a living landscape created by the growth of various species of *Sphagnum* moss, each adapted to a different degree of ground wetness and with an individual growth form. Patterns of hummocks and hollows can develop, with the hollows forming water-filled pools in a bewilderingly complex mosaic. The impression gained from an aerial view is stunning – that of a jewelled landscape with the pools appearing to 'flow' in a series of concentric arcs. Variations in the patterns occur throughout Britain and the reasons for them are an intriguing mystery. Similar features can be found on the tundra of the USSR and northern America. But the Flow Country pools are most unusual because of their formation on blanket bog. The flows should be regarded as a uniquely British inheritance to the world environment. Instead, large tracts have been converted to the highly artificial habitat of conifer plantations.

Ploughing in the flows has gone right up to the edge of patterned pools and the hydrology of only eight of the 41 water catchments in the region is now unaffected by forestry. Bruce Sandison (1986), an expert on fishing in the region is outraged by what has happened and thinks that it 'will be remembered for exactly what it is – one of the great acts of vandalism of the late 20th century'.

Further effects on plants and animals

Initially the young conifers are no more than lines of small bushes between the residual strips of ground vegetation. Wetland plants such as sundew, butterwort and bog bean are immediately affected by drying of the peat surface after ploughing. But because the land

Figure 3.4 *The patterned land – pools on the bogs of the Flow Country, rimmed by winter ice*

Figure 3.5 *The destruction of the Flow Country – the ploughlines of blanket afforestation ruin one of Britain's most important and evocative wildlife habitats*

has been fenced off, and the grazing pressure from deer or sheep reduced, grasses and ericaceous shrubs of drier ground such as flying bent, heather and bilberry can grow taller and thicker.

The change in animal life is dramatic and some of the open country birds disappear at once, with others lingering for a few years. These casualties include lapwing, wheatear, skylark, golden plover, dunlin, snipe, greenshank, redshank, curlew, red grouse and meadow pipit. Some of these birds make a particular contribution to human enjoyment of the uplands and the cascades of lark song, or the eerie, plaintive call of the golden plover, are part of the magic of the hills. Several of these species have already suffered significant decreases of their total British nesting populations through afforestation, and the loss becomes greater with each passing year.

The plight of bird populations in the Flow Country is especially significant and up to 20 per cent of their nesting and feeding habitat has already been destroyed by blanket afforestation. Rare birds which are threatened in the flows include the elegant black-throated diver with an estimated 150 British breeding pairs, and the inappropriately named common scoter with just 75–80 British breeding pairs. The bird community as a whole is of great interest as a southern outlier of a northern tundra type not found elsewhere in Britain or, indeed, south of Scandinavia. The wading bird populations are especially important, both nationally and internationally. The golden plover and the dunlin are virtually absent in the rest of the European Economic Community (EEC), and Britain also supports the entire European population of the greenshank south of the Baltic. While these and other birds could be regarded as the fringes of large and widespread northern populations, the evidence is that their British populations are genetically and physiologically distinct and largely isolated as breeding groups.

By contrast, the wildlife value of songbirds which colonise plantations is less important. During their early years the young, bushy trees play host to open-ground songbirds such as whinchat and stonechat, and birds of open woodland including tree pipit, willow warbler and whitethroat. The denser growth of the residual ground vegetation also allows an increase in the numbers of small mammals, followed by an influx of predators such as short-eared owls and, sometimes, kestrels. Hen harriers may also establish localised colonies during this limited phase of the crop rotation. But the benefit to all of these birds is purely ephemeral.

As the trees close canopy their ability to sustain the wildlife of open ground plummets. Birdlife soon becomes restricted to the upper branches and the edges of the plantation and is limited to species such as goldcrests, coal tits, chaffinches and pigeons,

Figure 3.6 *Afforestation in the Flow Country threatens the habitat of the beautiful black-throated diver – only 150 pairs are estimated to breed in Britain*

which are all common and widespread in Britain. On the positive side, a few formerly uncommon birds such as siskins and crossbills have become locally common because of the spread of afforestation. But the overall effect is the replacement of specialised upland bird communities which had a high proportion of waders. Future diversification of plantation birds is limited by the absence of ground vegetation, a shrub layer, and dead wood and nesting sites. The contrast with an ancient semi-natural woodland could hardly be more complete.

Particularly worrying is the loss of open-ground predatory birds caused by blanket afforestation. Watson *et al* (1987) estimate that in the south-west highlands of Scotland, as a result of afforestation already carried out, the population of golden eagles will decline to 50 per cent of 1960 levels by the year 2000. The potential decline in West Lochaber, Skye and Mull will also be about 50 per cent if afforestation is allowed to proceed without constraints. Ravens are so dependent on sheep carrion that they cease nesting at once and usually vacate the area as soon as the conifers close into a thicket. The merlin becomes replaced by the sparrowhawk, but buzzards are variably affected, and there is local colonisation of more mature conifers by the reintroduced goshawk.

Once the conifer crop is clearfelled, ground vegetation can reestablish, but the original semi-natural plant communities are not restored. New colonists, associated with habitats subjected to human disturbance, such as rosebay willowherb, foxglove and brambles may appear. Songbirds recolonise these felled areas but populations of open moorland birds, especially waders are minimal. Some open-ground species recolonise, but at much lower density than previously and this phase only lasts until the replanted trees close back into a thicket again.

Another disturbing aspect of blanket afforestation with worrying implications for the population of open-country birds is an apparent 'edge effect'. Stroud and Reed (1986) found that moorland waders have a tendency to avoid nesting anything from one-quarter to half a mile (400–800 m) away from plantation edges, which seriously increases the impact of afforestation on their populations. Other problems may be caused by the tendency of unkeepered plantations to harbour populations of foxes and crows, which can allow increased predation of the eggs and young of birds nesting on the moorland beyond.

While examples of various open-ground plant communities may persist within the forest, along rides, roadsides or other unplanted ground, they often become modified by the changed conditions. They mostly occur as fragments and in quite unnatural, often linear, configurations which give a wholly unsatisfactory representation of their previous extent (Ratcliffe 1986). Wet-ground vegetation tends to dry out through lowering of the water table. Many plant species have declined in abundance through afforestation, and wet-ground species have been particularly adversely affected. Rare and local species which have decreased include bog rosemary, cranberry, tall bog sedge, dwarf birch, English sundew, grass of Parnassus and intermediate bladderwort. Many species have been reduced in abundance, but still remain common and widespread. The plants which have increased within open ground in the forests are particularly those of disturbed habitats, and not true woodland species. The flora of the stands of conifers tends to be especially restricted or, in the case of unthinned areas, lacking altogether.

The wildlife changes brought about by afforestation thus involve a balance sheet of losses and gains. How this balance sheet is interpreted depends on one's standpoint, but nature conservationists are bound to rate uncommon and declining communities and species more highly than those which are commonplace and increasing. They must also be concerned when the extent of replacement of open-ground habitats by conifer forest has every appearance of being an open-ended process in any district.

Effects on soil and water

As soon as intensive ploughing and drainage are carried out there is a sharp increase in the rate of run-off of rainwater from the catchment. In the years that follow, streams and rivers fed from ploughed forests become more irregular in their flows. During wet weather they are subject to well-known, increased spates of water flow, followed by rapid subsidence to less than normal flows. The overall picture is complicated, and despite increased variations in flow, the total amount of water leaving the catchment when the plantation matures is reduced, which may affect supplies to reservoirs.

The extent of soil or peat exposed by the ploughs, on sloping ground in areas of high rainfall, makes it inevitable that the amount of sediment carried into streams and rivers is increased. Robinson and Blyth (1982) found sediment loads soared to 50 times their previous level during drainage operations, and took several years to settle down to a level that was still four times greater than prior to afforestation. Such increases in sediment also lead to more rapid silting-up of lakes and pools further downstream. These problems are undoubtedly compounded by the greater erosion caused by increased spates of streams.

Vast new plantations are also a source of increased pollution. The mass of evergreen conifer foliage acts as an efficient filter or 'scrubber' for the existing atmospheric pollution which is responsible for acid rain. The pollution is trapped by the foliage and is washed off by rain and mist, eventually draining into watercourses which may become 14 times as acid as they were previously, as research in the headwaters of the Severn and the Wye has shown (Newson 1985). Further pollution occurs from the inevitable leakage of the phosphate, nitrogen and potassium fertilisers which are routinely applied to upland plantations, into the wider environment, especially streams and lakes. These fertilisers, together with pesticides, are added in bulk to those few locations in the countryside where they were hitherto largely absent. The conifers also have an acidifying effect on the soil on which they grow, by the accumulation of a surface layer of needle litter.

Effects on aquatic plants and animals

The drastic changes to the flow, chemistry and sediment load of watercourses have an impact on the plants and animals that inhabit them. High levels of acidity in water are harmful, and many researchers have confirmed that the extra acidification caused by plantations is an increasing problem to aquatic life, including fish.

Catches of salmon in the heavily forested catchment of the River Fleet in Galloway have been reduced by one third, while sea trout catches have been decimated in a decade (Drakeford 1979, 1982). When Harriman and Morrison (1982) planted fertilised salmon eggs into Loch Ard streams, those in forest streams died rapidly, while a high proportion of eggs in open moorland streams survived. The increase in scouring and sediment also adversely affects salmon and trout by disrupting the beds of gravel that they use for spawning. Other researchers found a strong correlation between the recent decline in the number of adult Atlantic salmon caught in some districts of Scotland, and the amount of afforestation in the upland waters where the nursery streams occur (Egglishaw, Gardiner and Foster 1986).

When blanket afforestation encroaches too closely on streams the shade and needle litter inevitably reduce the growth of the aquatic plant life which is at the start of the food chain. The disappearance of the familiar streamside bird of the uplands, the dipper, from the upper 5 miles (8 km) of the river Irfon in South Wales has been correlated with the loss of aquatic invertebrates. The birds were plentiful during the 1950s before a large proportion of the catchment was afforested.

Effects on landscape

By its very nature, blanket afforestation spreads over vast areas of countryside. Where there are low, rolling hills, the plantations will spread right over their tops. If the hills exceed 1,800 ft (550 m) then the problem of an abrupt, harsh plantation edge on a contour across the hillside is created, to which there is no real solution, so great is the contrast between the dark mass of evergreen trees and the subtle variations of the hill. This problem occurs at even lower elevations on more exposed sites. Perhaps the most visually acceptable plantations are those on more rugged terrain where the fortuitous occurrence of rocky outcrops can give an impression of a more natural edge to the planting.

Given the insurmountable problems of making blanket afforestation acceptable in the landscape, the tactics of the forestry lobby are interesting. The first course is to improve landscape design, and after 28 years of mounting controversy, the FC appointed Dame Sylvia Crowe as its official advisor. As observed in 1986: 'Some of the least attractive forests are those consisting of large areas of single-age monoculture. This statement is particularly true of unbroken conifer plantations, because these discourage undergrowth, resulting in a diminution of wildlife. Such plantations are also visually monotonous.'

The second tactic is to grasp the Sitka by the needles and admit there have been mistakes – in the past. There is ample scope for these admissions and a queue of foresters and landowners is prepared to make them (Table 3.1). It seems to have developed into a

Table 3.1: *How forestry has made mistakes in the past*

'We applaud the frank admission of past mistakes –
from which forestry is only now beginning to recover.'
Scottish Woodland Owners Association
F&BT September 1979

'It is still not difficult to find examples of appalling
landscape planning and some ecologically disastrous
planting schemes.'
A. Moncrieff *EFG Magazine* 1985

'There is no denying that some of the pre-war, and some
of the post-war, planting was unsympathetic to say the
least. There were reasons for the choice of both area and
species, notably the economic necessity to plant every
last acre, and as quickly as possible . . .'
A. Rowan 1986

'The large-scale and sometimes environmentally
unsympathetic planting of earlier coniferous plantations
created a strong antipathy to commercial forestry in this
country.'
Country Landowners Association 1986

'Modern foresters are not insensitive: they have learned
from mistakes of the past. They are already conscious of
the need to avoid hard edges to plantations.'
F&BT September 1986

'Mistakes have undoubtedly been made in the past, with
monoculture forests in conspicuous places, but in the
past 15 to 20 years, foresters have become far more
aesthetically aware.'
Duke of Buccleuch 1988

comforting ritual, allowing them to make the debatable claim that things are better now. Many conservationists, however, feel that afforestation in the Flow Country is an on-going mistake of grand proportions, made in the full knowledge of all that was wrong.

Effects on access

Walkers in the hills usually feel that conifer plantations are an unwelcome and extraneous addition to what they habitually regard as a more natural environment. The plantations also provide a daunting physical barrier of dense, rough branches bearing sharp needles. One forestry surveyor finds that protection for the whole of his head and neck is necessary, using a clear acetate face shield combined with a hood fixed onto his jacket, which gives him protection from abrasion (*F&BT* January 1986).

Further problems are faced by walkers because the pace of afforestation is so great that Ordnance Survey maps are often, and frustratingly, out of date. Neither do such maps always show any of the rides or roads that would allow a way to be navigated between the trees. Traditional access routes to Munros (Scottish hills over 3,000 ft (914 m) in height) including Ben More in Perthshire and Beinn a Bheithir, have been blocked by conifers with wholly inadequate provisions for letting walkers through. Hills over 2,000 ft (609 m) in the Scottish lowlands, listed by Percy Donald and known as 'the Donalds' have been particularly badly affected by afforestation. Access onto Cairnsmore of Fleet in Galloway can be an epic battle through massed conifers. These ordeals may begin to pale into insignificance if the current trend towards electric fencing against deer and sheep continues. The much lauded recreational facilities in FC forests, mostly consist of an invitation to be confined to a picnic site, or a marked walk along a road or ride. As the Forestry Committee of Great Britain (1971) put it, plantations are 'necessarily inaccessible to the public'. This is despite the fact that the public pays most of the costs of establishing them.

The view from the forestry lobby

Foresters often stress that open land is left within their plantations in any case. They may well be referring to the standard 15 per cent reduction, suggested in FC timber yield tables, to allow for unproductive areas such as roads and rides. It should, however, be quite obvious that such fragments of open land are totally inadequate representations of what is lost. In particular, the geometric, linear configuration of roads and rides through plantations, with a 'wall' of coniferous plantation on either side, reduces any value they might have for wildlife even further.

The forestry lobby also makes use of a corruption of the diversity criterion, used to assess the importance of a site for wildlife, by claiming that conifer plantations diversify the upland environment on which they are imposed. But the new forests are highly artificial, and a similar diversification could be achieved by planting rhododendrons. The influx of predators to feed on the increased small mammal populations in some young plantations, and the songbirds that also benefit from afforestation, are also fertile sources of obfuscation. The first is a temporary phenomenon of the first rotation of the tree crop, and the second cannot be regarded as any adequate substitute for specialised bird communities that may have been replaced.

Foresters adopt the attitude that conservation does not begin until a forest has been planted, and this is implicit in publications such as *The Forestry Commission and Conservation* (1986 b). There has been progress in encouraging the planting of broadleaves, and in leaving unploughed margins along streamsides, in an attempt to reduce sedimentation problems, but these are mere palliatives. Foresters are justly proud of ponds they may create but must realise that such largely cosmetic features do not excuse or mitigate the problems caused by blanket planting.

The conservation view

The NCC is the government body which promotes nature conservation and gives advice to government and all those whose activities affect Britain's wildlife and wild places. Its review of the impact of forestry, *Nature Conservation and Afforestation in Britain* (1986), is a seminal work, and provides a carefully constructed condemnation of current forestry practice and policy. The conservation work of the NCC follows two basic approaches. Firstly, it identifies sites that require special protection for their nature conservation worth. The most important sites are designated as National Nature Reserves which are managed primarily for wildlife. A second tier of sites is protected as Sites of Special Scientific Interest (SSSIs). Here the existing land-use can usually continue as a primary concern, but the NCC is consulted prior to proposed developments that might adversely affect the wildlife interest. The total area of SSSIs and Reserves covers about 8 per cent of Britain, and could increase slightly. The second basic approach of the NCC is to promote conservation in the wider countryside by means of advice and persuasion.

The SSSIs have attracted much animosity, and are not helped by their clumsy title which suggests elitism, obscurity and officiousness. (Perhaps Natural Heritage Sites would be more widely accepted?) The designation of SSSIs is frequently attacked by forestry lobbyists, and other landowning interests, who claim that they sterilise the countryside and obstruct the rightful freedom of people to do what they want with their own land. The first charge is difficult to comprehend when applied to the protection of diverse and dynamic living communities of plants and animals. In answer to the second charge, a large proportion of SSSIs protects features such as mountain tops, coastal sites, geological features and river systems where the pressure for development may be low. In any case, most development proposals would not be countenanced if it were not for the availability of public money in the form of grants and subsidies, as with afforestation schemes. And the beneficiary of this largesse is the private landowner or occupier and not usually the nation. A proportion of SSSIs are already controlled by conservation interests, so that the blanket resentment of foresters and landowners could be considered excessive. It is important that SSSIs are large enough to meet their objectives, and in the uplands they may have to be 10,000–40,000 acres (4,000–16,000 ha) in size to encompass the large-scale variations of soil and vegetation that are found, and to protect the large territories needed by birds such as golden eagles.

Forestry interests often seem to misunderstand the essential purpose of the system of SSSIs. It is crucial to appreciate that the chosen sites are simply intended to protect an exemplary sample of the whole range and variety of natural habitats in Britain. Far from only protecting rare features, examples of characteristic and typical habitats are also included. The rationale is not that the whole of the rest of the countryside can then be the subject of intensive exploitation without a thought for conservation, which would be disastrous for wildlife. The future for nature conservation must lie in sound policies and controls which allow a balance of land-uses to co-exist, and wildlife to have a place throughout the countryside. Blanket afforestation is causing problems because the point of balance is being reached or exceeded in great tracts of the uplands, and the key problem is how to find a way to ensure that some open land remains outside of the existing SSSIs. The forestry lobbyists seem to believe it is no responsibility of theirs to take account of what they are destroying, so convinced are they that what they create is so much better.

The concern of the NCC (1986) is summed up as: 'Blanket afforestation over large areas is inimical to nature conservation, even if no specially important areas are planted, since it reduces open ground wildlife and habitats on such a massive scale within a single district.' The words of Ogilvy (1986) confirm that a clash with expansionist forestry interests seems inevitable: 'In the year 2026, I do not foresee blocks of forestry on a moorland landscape, but the stark moorlands of SSSIs and common grazings isolated in a forest scene.'

One of the most deplorable aspects of the forestry lobby's lack of concern about the environmental impact of afforestation, is that it has largely abandoned associated research to outside bodies. It has been up to the NCC and RSPB to investigate the effects on wildlife, and bodies such as the Institute of Hydrology have been left to investigate the effects on sedimentation and acidification. One of the root causes of this problem is the dual role of the FC as Forestry Authority and Enterprise, which is discussed in later chapters.

Part Two

The Rise of the Forestry Lobby

= 4 =

The Afforestation Industry

The Forestry Commission

It is wise not to underestimate the power of the FC. Since 1945 the area of its plantations has more than quadrupled, to over 2.2 million acres (0.9 ha) with a value of £1,609 million, as reported by the National Audit Office (NAO) (1986). The FC has become the UK's largest landowner with control over almost 10 per cent of Scotland, and approaching 4 per cent of the UK land area. It has the legal status and civil service trappings of a government body, but has an unusual management structure which contributes to its role as an active member of the forestry lobby (Chapter 8).

The FC is heavily dependent on public subsidy, voted to it as an annual grant-in-aid from parliament, which amounted to £52.5 million in 1986/87. Between 1946 and 1986 the total grant-in-aid amounted to £2,058 million, a colossal sum which would have been higher except for the income from recent plantation sales (NAO 1986). The continuing subsidies inevitably prompted the question at the 1987 House of Commons Public Accounts Committee (PAC) as to when the FC would be able to get off the annual drip of state aid, especially as this had been envisaged as happening after the first rotation of tree crops. The FC director-general replied that he did not see this happening until a couple of decades into the next century.

The work of the FC is split between two roles. It is both a Forestry Enterprise and a Forestry Authority, and each requires a heavy subsidy.

The Forestry Enterprise

The main role of the FC has been as a Forestry Enterprise, set up to grow timber to be sold to the wood processing industries. It produces about 60 per cent of home-grown timber, specialising in the bulk production of low-value crops, which earned it an income from timber sales of £71.7 million in 1986/87. Unfortunately this income was £34.3 million less than its operating costs, and the difference was bridged by public subsidy through the grant-in-aid.

41

The Forestry Authority

The second role of the FC is as Forestry Authority. Here it advises the government on policy, undertakes research, provides technical advice, and operates a system of felling licences and plant health controls. Most significantly, in terms of environmental impact in the uplands, it pays grants to encourage private sector afforestation. Since 1945 the FC has paid out £203 million, on about 1,850 sq miles (479,000 ha) of mostly coniferous, private plantations (NAO 1986). During 1986/87 a total of £7.3 million was paid out in grants (FC 1987 d).

Payment of an FC planting grant is subject to a system of voluntary consultation which is controlled by the Authority itself (see Chapter 9). If planting grants are approved the land is said to be 'forestry cleared', and it immediately increases in value and saleability. Despite this, no charge is made for the services of the Forestry Authority.

The fatal flaw

The division of the FC into Authority and Enterprise is at the heart of the problems of forestry in Britain, as will become clear in later chapters, and has been described as the 'fatal flaw' and as 'a Gilbertian situation . . . which should be ended forthwith' (*F&BT* June/July 1976). A former Conservative Shadow Minister of Agriculture has wondered whether the dual role was 'entirely satisfactory or fair' (*F&BT* March 1978).

On the hills and moors the dual role has achieved nothing more than an unimaginative and ill-conceived blanket of afforestation over the poorest land for growing trees. The publicly-owned Forestry Enterprise has pursued a vested interest in planting as much land as possible, while the Authority is supposed to have promoted afforestation by a competing private sector and controlled it at the same time. Both roles frequently have to be played by a single FC officer, making forestry decisions over several counties.

The FC grant schemes

Grants towards the cost of private planting were introduced in 1921, to help private landowners to replant woodlands felled during the First World War. The grants covered about 25 per cent of the costs but the uptake was low and only 123,500 acres (50,000 ha) were planted in the next 20 years.

The Second World War saw further extensive fellings of private forests, and a new grant scheme was introduced in 1948 with the specific intention of encouraging the replanting of felled areas. Under this Dedication Scheme landowners entered a formal legal agreement with the FC to dedicate particular pieces of land to forestry. They were also required to maintain full management plans, and were paid planting grants and an annual management grant in return. The original scheme was modified to form the Basis II and III Dedication Schemes, and although they are all now closed to new applicants, grants are paid under these schemes to the present day.

The search for a less cumbersome and expensive means of grant aid, under the guidance of Sir Derek Rayner, led to the replacement of Basis III by the Forestry Grant Scheme (FGS) in October 1981. This did away with formal legal agreements, detailed management plans and annual management grants. Only the planting grant remained.

Until forestry's 'big bang' in 1988 the grant schemes never provided the primary motivation of private blanket afforestation – that was driven by tax avoidance. None the less, the forestry lobby has always seen planting grants as a crucial measure of confidence that the government is prepared to continue to support its industry through public subsidy. This is confirmed by the director-general of the FC, giving evidence to the PAC: 'If grant aid were in some way to be diminished or taken away that would certainly be taken as a signal that there was no confidence in forestry' (1987). It seems that the whole of the forestry industry is hooked on the drip of state aid, and not just the FC itself. Tilhill Forestry made it clear that 'the private sector sets store on the level of grant-aid as a confidence indicator, a tangible expression of the government's will to encourage private forestry' (*F&BT* April 1981).

Any changes to the grant system produce jitters in the forestry lobby. When the closure of the Basis II Scheme was announced after the critical Treasury Review of 1972, there was a last minute rush of 118 applications covering 35,200 acres of land (14,250 ha), which were still being considered two years later. There were great doubts about the Basis III Scheme which followed because of its stated aims of securing environmental benefits, and possibly public recreation and access, which were added to appease conservation and amenity interests. Fears grew that private afforestation would cease altogether. But it soon became clear there was nothing more than an obligation to enter into innocuous discussions with the local authority about access if requested, and no danger of public access being imposed, so that afforestation soon began to flourish again.

In time foresters became fond of Basis III and when this in turn was replaced by the simplified FGS, hostile judgements were pronounced by the Institute of Chartered Foresters, the Association of Professional Foresters and the Timber Growers. One spokesman said the change was 'pure folly and a short-sighted cost saving exercise . . .' (F&BT April 1981). Confidence soon recovered, however, and 49,222 acres (19,920 ha) were planted in Britain under the FGS in 1986/87 (FC 1987 d).

The next change to the FC's planting grants came in 1988 when the FGS was replaced by the Woodland Grant Scheme (WGS), and planting grants were massively increased to compensate for a change to the system of forestry tax incentives. These changes came as a cataclysmic shock to the forestry lobby, before which any previous qualms about tinkering with the grant system paled into insignificance (see Chapter 6). Conscious of the afforestation industry's nervousness about changes to the grant and tax incentives, the government went to great lengths to stress its continued support for afforestation, but this was cold comfort for the forestry lobby.

It is easy to lose sight of the fact that the original Dedication Scheme was intended to allow the replanting of woodlands, mostly broadleaved and in the lowlands, which were felled in the Second World War. Forty years, and several modifications of the grant scheme later, the original purpose became completely corrupted. The principal achievement of all of the schemes simply became the blanket afforestation of bare land in the hills with conifers. By 1970 at least 83 per cent of activity was new planting, rather than replanting, and the 1972 Treasury Review decided that the Dedication Scheme had clearly outlived its original purpose. But so powerful had forestry become, that blanket afforestation with grant aid continued remorselessly.

The present position is demonstrated by the replies of the FC director-general to the PAC (1987): 'It is very crucial to the continuing confidence of the forest products industry in this country that they see a continuation of expansion . . . There would be quite considerable concern amongst investors in those industries if it were to be seen that new planting in this country were to cease or diminish significantly.'

Finally, it is important to emphasise the size of grant schemes. It is just 40 to 60 major plantings every year, each covering 250–4,000 acres of land (100–1,600 ha) that sustain blanket afforestation. Mather and Murray (1986) found the average size of a sample of planting schemes in Scotland was 363 acres (147 ha), despite the distortion produced by a large number of small schemes.

They found that the 6 per cent of schemes over 1,235 acres (500 ha) occupied 23 per cent of the total sample area, but there were nearly five times as many schemes in the 25–123 acre category (10–50 ha) which made up just 6 per cent of the total area.

The taxation of woodlands

A basic aim of the taxation system is 'fiscal neutrality'. This is an attempt to ensure that the burden of taxes falls fairly, and with equal effect, on all industries. Inevitably this leads to different industries being treated in different ways, according to their circumstances.

Forestry is an unusual industry with many unique factors to be considered when deciding on how it should be taxed fairly. Trees take a very long time to grow to maturity, up to 70 years for conifers and 110 years or more for most broadleaves, so that a succession of human generations might have to tend a woodland before the trees are ready for felling. Also, trees often have a low financial value. The timber in a single, average quality, broadleaved tree might only be worth £30–50 when extracted to a roadside, after 100 years of growth. An acre of average broadleaved woodland, land and trees, can be bought for just £300–700. The management of such woodlands can be a financial burden on their owners, although the trees may provide incomparably greater benefits to the wider community in terms of their value for landscape and wildlife.

Before the 1988 Budget the special needs of forestry were recognised under income tax Schedule B, which originated in legislation dating back to 1915. This was the normal way of taxing a woodland, and when a woodland changed ownership it automatically became taxed in this way. Under Schedule B there was no liability to pay tax on income received from timber sales, or on any grants received. The only liability was to a tiny annual charge, levied on one third of the rental value of the land alone, in its notional unimproved state. This worked out to be so ludicrously low, perhaps £0.15 per acre (£0.37 per ha) or less, that it was hardly ever collected by the Inland Revenue. Few people could have objected to rewarding the owners of a broadleaved woodland in this way, where any income obtained from felling is often absorbed by the costs of replanting.

However justified Schedule B may have been, its operation was completely obscure and archaic. The 1988 Budget undertook a thoroughly refreshing simplification of the system of forestry taxation, by wholly removing commercial woodlands from the scope of income tax and corporation tax. This meant that income from timber sales was still tax free, but without any of the contorted calculations of Schedule B.

Other tax concessions recognising the unique nature of forestry seem to be fair. Intensive lobbying by foresters in the 1970s led to concessions on CTT, which might otherwise have been levied repeatedly during the growing cycle of a single woodland. This tax has been replaced by Inheritance Tax (IHT), where forestry qualifies for 50 per cent business assets relief, and deferment in the case of a transfer on death.

The drawback to all such concessions is that they have created markets for the purchase of woodlands for no other reason than relief from CTT and IHT. The constantly shifting ownership of such woodlands that ensues, does not benefit tree growth or long-term management, although forestry companies, financial advisors and solicitors all get their fees. Finally, Capital Gains Tax is not levied on the increase in value of the trees, only on any increase in the value of the land.

Afforestation for tax avoidance – the tax loophole

None of the above incentives, deserved as they might be, are what drove private blanket afforestation of the hills. This was due to a tax loophole. Although the loophole was closed in the 1988 Budget, it had operated for 36 years, and it would be difficult to understate its crucial role in the development of British forestry. It was responsible for the very nature and location of private afforestation, the creation of the afforestation companies, and the structure of the forestry lobby.

When the tax opportunity became apparent, Economic Forestry Group (EFG) was formed in the early 1950s. When a founder of Fountain Forestry heard of the loophole, he 'at first reacted with disbelief to the suggestion that the government actively encouraged private forestry investment by offering tax relief to people who used part of their income to plant trees for future timber production.' After further consultations a syndicate was formed to purchase two woodlands in Somerset and Gloucestershire, where 16.5 acres (6.7 ha) were planted during 1955–56: 'To their astonishment tax relief was allowed on the money spent!' (*F&BT* June 1982).

The astonishing tax loophole was that the money spent on creating plantations on bare land could be taxed under income tax Schedule D. This is a conventional, widely applied tax schedule under which many businesses are taxed. When a loss is incurred in any one year, full tax relief can be obtained on income from other sources equal to the amount of the loss. All that a forestry investor needed to do to qualify for this lucrative source of tax avoidance, was simply to buy some land, pay an afforestation company to plant the trees, and sit back and wait for them to grow. This simple investment was treated as a business and all the money spent on tree planting was treated as a tax loss.

Forestry lobbyists made much of the fact that they were treated no differently to other businesses in the application of Schedule D. But the 1980 PAC felt that forestry subsidies should not be 'left to the fortuitous consequences of the exploitation of a tax loophole'.

The costs of tax avoidance

The cost of paying an afforestation company to fence a large block of hill land, plough and drain it, plant it with conifers and tend it for six to ten years, is on average £400 per acre (£1,000 per ha). Under the FGS the investor received an FC planting grant of almost £100 per acre (£250 per ha) which reduced the overall cost of the planting work to £300 per acre (£750 per ha) and this amount could then be claimed as a tax loss. If the investor was paying tax at 60 per cent on other income, then a full 60 per cent of the balance of the planting costs could be recovered from the Inland Revenue under the provisions of Schedule D. This brought the cost to the investor down to just £120 per acre (£300 per ha). Overall, 70 per cent of the costs of afforestation could be met by public subsidy during the tax year 1987/88 (Figure 4.1).

There were other important tax benefits for forestry associated with assessment under Schedule D. Although the capital purchase price of the land itself was not eligible for tax relief, if money was borrowed to buy the land the interest on the loan was fully tax relieved. This was of considerable benefit to top-rate taxpayers, for as the forestry brochures said, this made the investment more 'tax-efficient'. Capital expenditure on new roads and new fences in Schedule D woodlands was not eligible for full tax relief, but could be offset against other income at a rate of 4 per cent per year over 25 years, under the Capital Allowance Act.

Schedule D had one drawback for some long-term woodland owners, however. Any income from timber sales was subject to tax, and to avoid this, when a woodland became mature and started to generate timber income, a switch back to Schedule B had to be engineered. This could only be done by a change of ownership, for otherwise the election to Schedule D was irrevocable. A transfer to a spouse or children was a convenient way for many forestry investors to switch tax schedules, and avoid ever paying any tax on their trees.

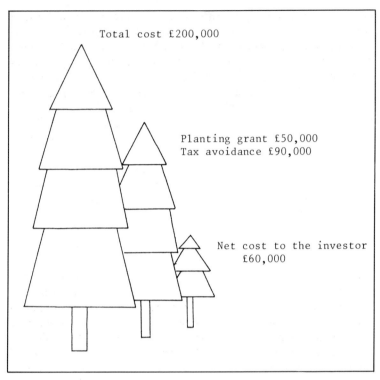

Total cost £200,000

Planting grant £50,000
Tax avoidance £90,000

Net cost to the investor
£60,000

Figure 4.1 *Subsidies to private afforestation through tax avoidance before the 'big bang' on a typical 500 acre (200 ha) planting scheme*

Despite its crucial importance, the true extent of tax avoidance in forestry was never widely known or even quantified. This was, of course, a considerable benefit to the forestry lobby, which was able to disguise the true extent of the public subsidies it received. The PAC (1987) was 'concerned at the lack of up-to-date and reliable information about its actual costs', and recommended that more information needed to be available. The NAO put the cost of tax concessions at £10 million a year, while EFG estimated the cost at perhaps £15 million (1986 a).

The new investors – the 60

Who were the investors responsible for the 40 to 60 major affores-tation schemes for tax avoidance each year? Only recently did the glare of publicity shine into a secretive world, where investors usually preferred to benefit from tax avoidance in discreet privacy. To investigate their activities was to attract taunts of jealousy, emotion or left-wing political bias from the forestry lobby. But their forestry operations need to be understood as a key part of the expansion of blanket afforestation which depended on their continued willingness to invest. Although the tax avoidance loophole which lured such investors into forestry was abruptly closed, many will retain ownership of their plantations for up to another 10 or 15 years, before selling them to get the return on their investment. Some will also benefit from the transitional arrangements that allow tax avoidance for existing woodland owners to continue until 5 April 1993.

Mather (1987) found that the great majority of personal forestry schemes are between 247 and 1,235 acres in size (100 and 499.9 ha), and that the average size of a personal forestry investment in Scotland is 485 acres (196 ha). A good quality piece of bare land of that size could easily have cost over £155,000. The investor then had to find almost £200,000 to pay to have the land planted by an afforestation company.

Wealth on such a scale is restricted to a very small proportion of Britain's population, especially when a forestry investment usually only accounts for a limited proportion of a prudent investor's portfolio. It is estimated that 1,000 to 2,000 new investors were recruited to forestry over 25 years, or just 40 to 80 individuals each year (*F&BT* April 1981). A leading firm of forestry surveyors and valuers pointed out that in one year it acted for the top ten earners in the City of London (*Sunday Times* 20 September 1987), and that of Britain's top 20 earners, half turned out to be its clients (*F&BT* March 1987).

Some of the more well-known investors and their forestry operations have been extensively reported in the national press, providing much needed publicity for the wider forestry debate. Terry Wogan purchased two blocks of planting land in the Flow Country, amounting to about 1,250 acres (506 ha), for a total of over £88,000. Other Flow Country investors include Alex Higgins, 934 acres (378 ha) for £50,800 and Lady Shirley Porter, 1,712 acres (693 ha) for £80,000. Cliff Richard, the evergreen pop-star, sold 2,677 acres (1,083 ha) of his plantations in Wales for what may have been close to the asking price of £1 million. In addition to the celebrity names there was a substantial core of successful business people, doctors, dentists, accountants and barristers, who invested in forestry for tax avoidance.

The end of the tax year was a particularly hectic time for the afforestation companies and their clients. Many high-rate taxpayers did not know how much income was at risk to the taxman until the last few months of the tax year, and there was often a hectic search to buy a block of forestry land so that trees could be put in the ground before 5 April.

Absentee landowners

An inevitable consequence of tax avoidance forestry was that it introduced absentee landowners into the countryside, for top-rate taxpayers almost invariably earn their money far from the hills and moors of the uplands. Mather and Murray (1986) found that 70 per cent of individual owners of plantations in Sutherland, in the far north of Scotland, had home addresses in London or the Home Counties. 'The founders of EFG realised that . . . an excellent case could be made for forestry investment by absentee owners, as opposed to residential estate owners or farmers . . .' (*F&BT* April 1981).

The chairman of the Highlands and Islands Development Board (HIDB), wrote in the *EFG Magazine* (1984) that: 'We in the Highlands view with some concern the physical separation of land and the trees from the people who own them and have suffered a lot from the absentee landlord. But even absentee landlords have often spent some of their wealth in the Highlands and we welcome the mechanisms by which the private forestry investment companies are helping to channel money from new categories of investor into our forestry.'

It was the absentee investors who sustained private blanket afforestation. Forestry by existing landowners in the countryside tends to have a wider range of objectives including shelter, landscape improvement and sporting, and their generally lower incomes often ruled out tax avoidance as an incentive for afforestation. Mather and Murray (1986) found 63 per cent of a sample of afforestation schemes carried out by traditional estates were under 123 acres (50 ha) in size, compared to only 16 per cent of schemes carried out by individual or corporate owners. Also, only one in eight schemes by traditional estates exceeded 494 acres (200 ha) compared to one in four owned by the new investors.

The afforestation companies – the 'big four'

The afforestation companies grew out of the exploitation of a tax avoidance loophole, and this has shaped their whole outlook and method of operation. Their first task is to woo their clients, and prior to the 1988 Budget, the most important of these were the top-rate taxpayers. These wealthy individuals are generally protected by trusted financial advisers, and often value their privacy, so that the companies had to set up sophisticated sales operations, often based in the City of London.

The abolition of the tax avoidance loophole has meant that the companies are now urgently marketing afforestation to wealthy, potential clients in new ways. It is also likely that institutions such as pension funds will play an increasingly important role in tree planting in the uplands (see Chapter 6). Whoever their future clients are, a key, commercial objective of the companies is to be able to continue to carry out large, profitable, upland afforestation contracts.

The companies' search for new clients is a continual process. At the same time they are energetically involved in tracking down the 40 to 60 major afforestation schemes that become available each year, and preparing to negotiate purchase arrangements. Their art is to match the client, and his or her financial resources, to a suitably sized forestry planting site. The company then arranges for the client to buy the land. During the 1980s the entire British market for the purchase of private planting land has reached 37,000–50,000 acres (15,000–20,000 ha) per year, worth about £10–12 million. It is very important to note that the company doesn't normally buy the land itself, as this is not necessary for making profits and can create risks.

Once the purchase is complete the client pays the afforestation company to carry out the planting programme, and this is how the company builds up its turnover and generates profits. The total market in afforestation contracts is about £15–20 million per year, and this is what the companies are competing for. 'Tanarus' is a diarist in *F&BT* magazine who confirms the importance of planting contracts: 'Let there be none in any doubt that the larger forestry companies depend for their turnover, their profitability and their continued existence upon the contracting work arising from new afforestation' (*F&BT* March 1982).

The four main companies are EFG, Fountain Forestry, Tilhill Forestry, and Scottish Woodlands, and they dominate the market. Mather (1987) found that one or other of the four was involved in half of all private forests in Scotland, and thought that even this was likely to be a considerable understatement. Working with Murray (1986) he found the 'big four' were responsible for 72 per cent of a sample area of Scottish planting schemes.

Mather found a further 20 per cent of his sample was planted by a 'second tier' of operators, handling the planting of a smaller number of schemes. It is easy to agree with Mather in finding it alarming that 90 per cent of the private afforestation in Scotland in the decade since 1975 was shaped by 'a mere handful of individuals'.

The pension funds – the 35

The entry of the pension funds into the plantation market, and the rise of the afforestation companies, are the two key events which have shaped private afforestation. One of the first major woodland purchases by a pension fund took place when the Post Office fund paid £783,500 to acquire 6,500 acres (2,600 ha) of woodland managed by Fountain Forestry (*F&BT* January/February 1977). The decline of the CTT market for the purchase of plantations by private investors meant that prices were low at the time, and a number of funds soon entered the market. Taylor (1981) described 'a rather unedifying scramble into woodlands whose chief characteristic was availability rather than quality or suitability and at one stage in the late 'seventies almost any woodland of reasonable size attracted competitive bids from as many as eight different pension fund buyers.'

It has been estimated that 30 to 35 funds entered the market between 1975 and 1982, together with six insurance companies (*F&BT* June 1982). In general these financial institutions are secretive about their forestry activities. Their investment requirements and attitudes now play a key role in the afforestation industry in the hills. Unfortunately, it is huge blocks of even-aged, blanket afforestation that are of most interest to them.

One of the drawbacks to institutional investors is the 'small' annual plantation market of just £25–40 million. Taylor (1981) points out that: 'The vast Post Office fund, for example, merely dabbles a toe in the woodland market and, along with the really big funds, can only be expected to prick up its ears at a £5 million deal.' Pension funds seek to invest perhaps 2 to 5 per cent of their portfolios in forestry, and want to move their money around efficiently, so that £1 million properties are of most interest to them. A minimum size of investment is usually £250,000–400,000 involving a block of 500–1,000 acres of plantation (200–400 ha). Mather (1987) found the average size of corporate forestry holdings in Scotland was 1,258 acres (509.1 ha). The pension funds also like simple uniform areas that can be managed easily and cheaply, so that large, even-aged monocultures suit them fine.

After the initial rush into forestry the funds became more selective about their purchases. During the mid-1980s it was usual for just three or four funds to bid for a plantation, and there were even fears that the market could collapse when only one or two made bids for plantations that were on the market.

The pension funds also have a wider involvement in the structure of the forestry industry. British Gas and Midland Bank funds, together with the Prudential, were involved in the purchase of the Riddoch of Rothiemay sawmill and pension funds are also share-holders in Fountain Forestry. The other potential, institutional purchasers of plantations are the life assurance companies, which are taxed in a similar manner to private individuals.

The secondary market

The pension funds and life assurance companies provided an essen-tial market where tax avoidance planters could sell their newly-created plantations. A typical planting investor, perhaps a pop-star or a snooker player, does not want to wait 30 years for a return on the investment through felling timber. Instead, when a plantation reached about ten years of age, needing little further expenditure, and having exhausted its usefulness as a tax avoidance sink, it could be sold to an institution. The requirements of the funds dictated that the high-rate taxpayers who started the afforestation process were best advised to plant at least 500 acres (200 ha) of land to ensure they had a marketable plantation to sell in future years.

Low plantation prices

Because tax avoidance has never influenced the investment decisions of the pension funds, the value they put on a plantation has always been an accurate guide to its real worth. They treat the underlying land as a separate property investment in its own right, valued at the prevailing market price. The young conifers are valued accord-ing to the timber income likely to be received in future years. By discounting this income back to the present day, the institutions calculate what they can afford to pay for the crop to achieve a 4 or 5 per cent return from timber growth over a 20–30 year period.

The crop values which result, leaving aside the land price, are surprisingly low, as shown in Figure 4.2. It can be 10–15 years before a conifer crop is equal in value to the total costs of planting it. The people who planted such crops can only afford to sell them at such a low price because of the massive subsidy they formerly received through tax avoidance and which is now available through grants alone.

Market prices for plantations and other woodlands have been studied by R. Helliwell. He made an analysis of a list of woodland properties for sale and found that 60 per cent were valued at £400–600 per acre (£1,000–1,500 per ha) and less than 10 per cent were over £1,000 per acre (£2,500 per ha). These prices are for the land as well as the timber (*F&BT* May 1984).

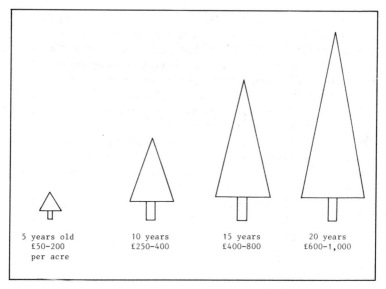

Figure 4.2 *Typical market values of upland conifer plantations per acre in 1986, excluding land value*

Another intriguing feature of the plantation market is that neat, uniform, ten-year old plantations are more easily sold, and at a relatively higher price, than twenty-year old plantations ready for first thinning.

Planting by the pension funds

As pension funds are tax exempt, they never benefited from tax avoidance on money they spent on afforestation. EFG (1986 b) advised the funds that it did not recommend them to buy bare land and plant it themselves. A different approach to pension funds was taken by Tilhill: 'Some of the more far-seeing . . . are already involved in planting on their own account as well as investing in existing woodlands and plantations' (*F&BT* April 1981).

Both Rolls Royce and Midland Bank pension funds are Tilhill clients who have planted bare land. The Midland Bank has been involved in one of the largest recent afforestation schemes in Scotland covering over 7,400 acres (3,000 ha) of land in Perthshire between Aberfeldy and Dunkeld (Mather 1987). Institutional investors seem to have accounted for 10 per cent of new planting in Scotland (PIEDA 1986).

The fact that pension funds plant bare land has not become as widely known as the planting activities of top-rate taxpayers. One pension fund was involved in an afforestation scheme that took

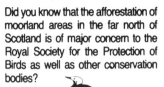

place in south Scotland without grant aid and ignoring the normal consultation process. Following forestry's 'big bang' it is likely that pension funds will come to carry out much more blanket afforestation in future years (see Chapter 6).

= 5 =

The Forestry Land Bubble

The drive for profits

Profits and profitability are the cornerstone of healthy, competitive industry. This is worth emphasising at the start, as the forestry lobby reacts strongly to criticism of its activities and labels them as commercial naivety or anti-business.

Working for an afforestation company leaves you in no doubt about the importance of planting contracts to its profitability. The larger the contract, the greater the turnover and the bigger the profit, and these simple commercial imperatives help to sustain the scale and pace of upland forestry. Afforestation companies charge around £400 per acre (£1,000 per ha) over a six to ten year period to carry out afforestation contracts for their clients. A typical 500 acre scheme (200 ha) might cost the client £200,000. Formerly, 70 per cent of this gross cost was refunded to the client by tax avoidance and grants, but the new FC grants, under the WGS, now refund just over 60 per cent of the costs.

Table 5.1: *The cost of a typical afforestation contract per acre (1 acre = 0.4 hectare)*

	Expenditure
Year 1	£225
Year 2	£ 80
Year 3	£ 40
Year 4	£ 25
Year 5	£ 15
Year 6	£ 15
	£400

It should be noted that the great majority of the costs are normally incurred in the first few years, involving the bulk of the fencing, ploughing and planting. Between year seven and felling timber at around 35 years, the costs drop to an annual maintenance charge of about £10 per acre (£25 per ha) each year.

The importance of planting bare land to an afforestation company can be shown by some simple calculations. A typical company might have a turnover of £10 million per year in its forestry activities, and plant 25 per cent of all afforestation contracts on about 10,000 acres of land (4,000 ha). On-going contracts at this level would generate a turnover of £4 million per year, or 40 per cent of total business handled. But the typical company also manages a further 250,000 acres (100,000 ha) of established plantations needing little further attention before they are felled. This area of plantations might generate just £10 per acre (£25 per ha) of turnover, totalling only £2.5 million. It is abundantly clear that planting contracts generate 40 times as much company turnover as managing the same area of existing plantations, and are also much more profitable, because the turnover is concentrated on a few, large, easily-managed contracts. It is much more difficult to make a profit from the lower, on-going maintenance costs of a large area of scattered plantations.

The tax-avoidance incentive also boosted the profitability of planting contracts to the afforestation companies. Investors spending money that would otherwise have gone to the Inland Revenue had a reduced incentive to scrutinise the costs of the contracts. Pension funds with no tax incentives were always more likely to look harder at the long-term costs of management of the established plantations that they own. The remainder of the £10 million turnover of a typical company could come from a variety of other contracting work, and interests in timber harvesting or nurseries.

Taylor (1987 b) identified the source of opposition to forestry: 'The persistence and the nature of attacks upon the industry have redoubled both in number and quality. Nearly all centre upon the activities of the forestry contracting companies who depend upon new planting for their profits but whose operations necessarily alter the landscape.'

The land price spiral

Land for afforestation is a limited commodity with a strictly finite supply. Because the companies depend for their profits on planting more and more of it, the price of such land during the era of tax avoidance afforestation rocketed. It is important to realise that it was competition between companies for land that forced up prices, even though it was their clients who actually bought the land: 'They are commercial operations depending upon profits derived from captive clients whose knowledge of costs, specifications and results is minimal. In a growing market this has the result of forcing up land prices as competition (not between potential woodland owners but between consultant/contractor companies), is created in order to obtain profitable management work' (*F&BT* July/August 1977).

Figure 5.1 shows the astonishing rise in forestry land prices which increased by an average of 15 per cent every year between 1950 and 1980, which was 7 per cent above the rate of inflation over the same period. In the early-1960s forestry land could be bought for just £10 per acre (£25 per ha), but by 1987 it had soared to £350 per acre (£865 per ha) in parts of Scotland and over £400 per acre (£1,000 per ha) in Wales.

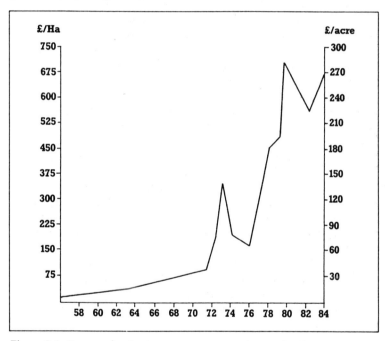

Figure 5.1 *Forestry land prices soar – average planting land prices 1958 to 1984*
Source: Syson 1985

In 1979 the director-general of the FC stated: 'Rapidly rising land prices are already in danger of getting out of touch with reality' (*F&BT* July 1979). And that was when average prices were a mere £200 per acre (£500 per ha). Hart (1987) pointed out that forestry land prices reflected the 'stockbroker syndrome' and were determined by competition rather than quality or location.

Forestry land prices in the uplands vary according to region and reached their highest in Wales, northern England and southern

Scotland. There was a tendency for prices to be lower in north and west Scotland. In Argyll prices reached £200–250 per acre (£500–620 per ha), on Skye £120–180 per acre (£300–450 per ha), and only £50–100 per acre (£125–250 per ha) in the Flow Country.

Throughout the period of tax-avoidance forestry there seemed to be no limit to the rise in planting land prices, as wealthy clients queued up to buy. The abrupt closure of the loophole had an immediate and devastating impact on forestry land prices (see Chapter 6).

Supply and demand

There is, of course, no earthly reason why the supply of planting land in the hills should ever have matched the demands of top-rate taxpayers for it as a tax-avoidance loophole. The decline in other tax-avoidance opportunities, and the expansion of the companies which used up the stock of planting land, fuelled rising land prices until the market became seriously overheated.

The arrival of the pension funds in the mid-1970s also gave a considerable twist to the price spiral. Hart (1987) records that during the 1970s plantations soared in value by at least five-fold. This led other observers to sound a warning: 'The huge sums of money coming into forestry have not expanded the area one whit but have merely driven prices ever higher and higher. One of these days, reality will come around, unless, of course, foresters get there first' (*F&BT* February 1981). It could be said that 'reality' arrived when the tax-avoidance loophole was closed in the 1988 Budget, bringing the land price crashing down.

The forestry lobby preferred to think that it operated, or should have operated, in a free market for planting land. It is hard to countenance this when the whole market was created, and distorted, by tax avoidance. When a piece of forestry land was actually planted it fell into a price limbo for several years and was worth less than its purchase price as bare land, because it was no longer any use for tax avoidance but too much still needed to be spent on the trees to attract a tax exempt pension fund. Another surprising distortion of the forestry market was that the value of bare planting land was catching up on the price of young plantations.

The role of the planting grant

It is quite incredible, unjust and unnecessary that the FC's flat-rate planting grant for large afforestation schemes is the same, whether 25 acres (10 ha) or 4,000 acres (1,600 ha) are planted. The grant is graduated for schemes under 25 acres (10 ha) but this principle is absurdly abandoned for larger schemes, despite the economies of scale that are possible.

During the latter period of tax avoidance afforestation, the grant for large schemes was almost £100 per acre (£240 per ha) under the FGS. The main achievement of this was simply to augment the effects of competition between the companies, and to inflate the price of hill land that was approved for planting with an FC grant. This was clearly illustrated by the planting of several schemes in south Scotland without grants, where the afforestation companies simply negotiated a price with the vendor of £100 per acre (£240 per ha) less for the land, to compensate for the loss of grant.

The mere granting of FGS clearance triggered a rise in the price of bare hill land, as noted by Moncrieff (1985): 'A number of potential planters were thus eventually disappointed and it was frustrating to see land selling at auction for £100 less than they would have paid simply because forestry clearance had been refused. The vendors also had reason to feel aggrieved and this situation hardly accords with government plans.'

Destabilisation of the land market

The package that afforestation companies sell to their clients comprises: land value + tree growth + rising timber prices = financial yield. There is clear evidence that much of the benefit of a forestry investment simply came from soaring land values, and these also had a destabilising effect on the balance of land-use in the hills.

The only other potential buyers who can compete for the purchase of land in the hills are the upland farmers. But they generally have ample hill land of their own, and are only usually interested in buying more of the scarce lowland in the valley bottoms. Also, farmers value their hill land in an entirely separate market to foresters according to the number of sheep it will carry. These factors mean that farmers cannot afford to pay a high price for hill land for farming purposes. The self same land which would have fetched over £300 per acre (£750 per ha) for forestry may be worth only £50–150 per acre (£120–370 per ha) to a farmer for sheep grazing. Hart (1987) notes that tax-avoidance forestry raised the market value of hill farming land cleared for planting by a factor of between two and six.

Such huge price rises put great pressure on farmers and estate owners to obtain forestry clearance on their hill land and to split up their landholdings when they came to sell. In the absence of adequate safeguards, this allowed blanket afforestation to continue its inexorable spread. The strains went on increasing because agricultural land prices actually fell, while forestry prices continued to climb. Afforestation began to take place on enclosed farmland in Devon and Cornwall sold for forestry at £400–550 per acre (£1,000–1,360 per ha).

When upland farms fell into the hands of speculators they were particularly prone to being split up for afforestation. Mather and Murray (1986) found clear evidence that forestry was associated with instability in land ownership. In over three-quarters of the sample afforestation schemes that they studied, the land had changed hands at least once in the previous ten years.

The value of land for wildlife and wilderness

When it comes to putting a price on land, conventional economics dictates that conservation and wildlife values lose out. How can the value of Britain's greenshank population be translated into pounds per acre? Even the NAO did not attempt to confront this challenge: 'Given the areas of present planting mostly on poor land in remote locations, it is appropriate, in assessing the return in economic terms, not to make any allowance for the price of land on the basis that the true economic cost to the nation of converting land to forestry is negligible. Much of the land currently used for forestry only has a value when put to agricultural or private forestry use.'

Some are clearly convinced that it is conservation that requires subsidies and not afforestation. The massive influx of public money, through tax avoidance or grants, that accompanies blanket afforestation is overlooked. Forestry lobbyists even seem to wonder how the nation could afford to do otherwise than subsidise their activities to the hilt.

The Timber Growers United Kingdom (TGUK) (1986) think that: 'We must decide how much of our land resource we (and our successors in the next century) will wish or can afford to "preserve" as wilderness, where wildlife conservation is preferred to development . . .' Jeffrey, Ashmole and MacRae (1986) propound similar views: 'We can no longer afford the luxury of vast tracts of the uplands being left barren for specialist interests which do not take into account a valuation of the assets.'

Planting poor land

The afforestation companies depend on planting land for their profits, and as the better land was used up, they inevitably spread onto poorer land. Unbridled subsidies also contributed to this unfortunate trend. Many of those who invested in forestry for tax avoidance had high incomes, but little capital available to buy the land that was needed for a planting scheme to avoid tax. As the companies' activities forced land prices up, it became ever more difficult for their clients to afford to buy the land in the first place. Poor, remote land then became easier to place with clients, simply because it was cheap. Clients got the same amount of tax-avoiding expenditure for a capital outlay of one third or less of the cost of better land, and the companies still got their afforestation contracts.

Tanarus gives a clear insight into the problems caused by the inflation of land prices: 'Vendors apart, it's hard to see who could benefit from expensive planting land. The FC certainly doesn't as they fall by the wayside relatively early in the race for a planting programme. The forestry companies don't as, the higher price of land, the smaller is their potential market among the wealthy and, depending as they do on a continuing planting programme for their profitable turnover, they begin to take on the doomed look of the dinosaur' (*F&BT* November/December 1978).

The problem of the price of forestry land was also recognised by Rankin: 'The main problem has been the price of land. Business and professional men frequently have good incomes with which to finance the cost of establishing a forest but they do not have the capital to buy the land. Suitable land for afforestation in the uplands of Britain may cost up to £300 per acre (£750 per ha) and, for any sizeable operation, this means quite a lot of money' (*F&BT Supplement* April 1982).

The move north

The subjective impression that the centre of afforestation activity gradually moved further north in Scotland, onto more remote land, is confirmed by Mather and Murray (1986). They found that the scale of movement was considerable, especially from 1980 onwards, and that the rate may even have been accelerating. In part this must have been due to some areas of west and south-west Scotland being saturated with conifers, but their results raise questions 'as to whether there is an optimal national pattern of forests (and, if so, as to how the changing pattern of recent years relates to it), and whether market forces, operating within the existing consultation procedures, are likely to lead to such a pattern'.

There is considerable disagreement within the forestry world about the planting of poor quality land, and this is explored in Chapter 9. Some companies will not carry out afforestation contracts in the Flow Country for example. Baguley (1985) warned that 'commercial forestry is now being pushed on to sites which have questionable tree growth potential because of exposure, elevation, soil types etc . . .'

Tanarus also expressed the problem: 'In the mid-seventies the thought of planting Caithness or Skye seemed a long way off . . . less than 10 years on and all these things have become a reality . . . In Perthshire and Argyll we are being asked to consider less and less thrifty lands (higher, more costly to develop and less productive acres) and the peaty wastes of Inverness and the far north' (*F&BT* February 1985).

Planting high land

The demand for planting land also pushed forests higher up the hills where tree growth is progressively restricted. A Royal Scottish Forestry Society meeting was told that: 'With the dearth of good planting land, foresters are seeking ground which, because of its elevation, would have been ignored a few years ago' (*F&BT* December/January 1981/82).

In its role as Forestry Authority, the FC will grant aid high-level planting as long as the trees survive and achieve the vague goal of 'a utilisable crop of timber'. Douglass (1986) has witnessed planting at high elevations on the Isle of Mull. He feels that trees are not

Figure 5.2 *Ugly plantations at the head of the Ettrick valley, Dumfries and Galloway, reach to nearly 1,800 ft (546 m) above sea level*

worth planting above 700 ft (210 m) on the island, but FC planting has gone up to 1,200 ft (365 m). The forestry workers who carry out the work 'will never be convinced that public money should have been wasted in planting them'. Douglass goes on to point out that the FC cannot admit to the error, which goes on being repeated. He also thinks that private planters may very well know they too are going over sensible heights, but 'they realise the Commission cannot disapprove their work without condemning itself'.

The correct altitudinal limit for tree planting varies according to location throughout Britain, and is lowest on exposed coasts and islands. But afforestation has been pushed up to 1,300–1,800 ft (400–550 m), onto poor, exposed land and over the tops of the hills. Doubts were expressed in 1979: 'Once again, quality has become secondary and we hope that some of those acquiring broad areas of high elevation Sitka spruce and lodgepole pine do not become disillusioned when in future the difficulty and expenses of maintaining growth, of access, stability, marketing and labour begin to present problems' (*F&BT* March 1979).

The landowners who sell

Upland landowners have always been the prime beneficiaries of the forestry land price spiral. The application for forestry clearance has to be made in the name of the landowner, so that it is farmers and estate owners who apply to the FC for approval to plant trees with grant aid. In the great majority of cases they have no intention of large-scale afforestation themselves, but once clearance is obtained they can sell the land to a forestry investor at a greatly increased price. The closure of the tax-avoidance loophole may have pegged back the price spiral, but its effects will still be felt in the uplands.

The afforestation companies are deeply involved in this process of forestry clearance. They seek to make contact with landowners, advise on the completion of the forms, and will supervise the consultations and negotiations. Their aim is to be able to negotiate a private purchase of the forestry cleared land by one of their clients, and then to be paid to carry out the afforestation contract.

At the end of 1984 the Buccleuch Heritage Trust purchased the 3,000 acre (1,200 ha) hill farm of Stennieswater, near Eskdalemuir, for £140,000. Less than three years later, having obtained forestry clearance for almost all of the land to be planted with conifers, it was sold to EFG (Estates) Ltd for the vastly increased sum of £776,000 (*Scotsman* 15 February 1988). The forestry company would then have split the land into parcels and sold it off to its clients.

Figure 5.3 *The forestry land price spiral – Stennieswater farm near Eskdalemuir in Scotland. The Buccleuch Heritage Trust bought the 3,000 acre (1,200 ha) farm for £140,000 in 1984. Less than three years later, having obtained forestry clearance from the Forestry Commission, the land was sold to EFG (Estates) Ltd for £776,000. Much of the land is now roaded, ploughed and planted with conifers*

The myth of agricultural re-investment

The FC itself recognises the forces that encourage farmers to sell out to absentee forestry investors and has spoken of 'the opportunity for an owner to cash in the land he does not need for his farming enterprise and re-invest it elsewhere' (*F&BT* March 1987).

Mather and Murray (1986) found that there was mention of re-investment in agricultural improvement in only one sixth of the cases they studied. They find this is understandable when financial stress may be the driving force leading to a decision to sell land in many instances. My personal experience in Scotland is that many farmers are likely to claim they will use the proceeds for farm improvements, in order to get a more sympathetic hearing from the Department of Agriculture which must agree large-scale forestry proposals, before the FC can give forestry clearance.

The crofters cash-in

The forestry land boom also threatened the continuance of traditional patterns of crofting in Scotland. Under the Crofting Reform (Scotland) Act of 1987, crofters have the right to buy their croft land for 15 times the annual rent, almost always a nominal sum. A number of crofters took the opportunity to buy their land cheaply, held on to it for a statutory five years, and then sold to forestry interests at greatly increased prices.

The *Scotsman* reports how one crofter bought his 3,972 acres (1,600 ha) from the government for £1,855. He was subsequently able to sell it to a Fountain Forestry client for £300,000. There is also pressure on landlords to resume croft land and then sell for forestry.

The secret land banks

So consistent and rapid was the rise in forestry land prices, that farmers and estate owners, who held land that was cleared for planting, owned a lucrative investment themselves. They could sit back and choose their time to sell to the eager forestry market. This explains why, out of a total of 541,522 acres (219,151 ha) of land in Britain cleared for planting under the FGS, only 150,145 acres (60,763 ha), less than one third of the total, had been planted at March 1986 (FC 1986 a).

The identity of the remaining land is regarded as confidential, for commercial reasons, and is kept a close secret by the FC. Anyone gazing across a landscape of plantations and bare hillsides in Scotland would do well to remember that much of the open land could already be earmarked for afforestation. At current rates of planting there is clearly enough land available to sustain private afforestation for six or seven years, contrary to the forest lobby's much proclaimed shortage of planting land. The precise location of the land is, of course, a source of considerable interest to the afforestation companies.

During the currency of the FGS, the FC itself has planted 211,532 acres (85,606 ha) throughout Britain. Some of this may have been FGS cleared land, but this still leaves a considerable amount in the secret land bank. In fact, a great deal of the land that the FC planted over the period came from its own secret land reserves, acquired in previous years. Its current programmes are only being maintained by eating into this reserve which decreased from 127,266 acres (51,504 ha) in 1982 to 74,599 acres (30,190 ha) in 1986.

= 6 =
Forestry's 'Big Bang' – the 1988 Budget

Tax avoidance – no way to run a forestry industry

It seems extraordinary that the whole course of private British forestry was determined by the vagaries of a tax-avoidance loophole for 36 years. The massive public subsidies provided for an extremely affluent minority to carry out blanket conifer planting in the uplands, causing serious problems for the conservation of landscape and wildlife, were always likely to become politically unacceptable. The forestry lobby was only too well aware of the dangers of publicising the tax-avoidance basis of private afforestation and the password tended to be: 'Don't draw attention to the tax reliefs' (*F&BT* April 1981). Taylor (1987 a) clearly foresaw the problems looming ahead for tax avoidance forestry which was vulnerable to political attack.

The attractions of tax-avoidance afforestation always had an extremely unhealthy dependence on the prevailing tax rate. When tax rates, including the unearned income supplement, reached 98 per cent during the 1970s, then a grotesque 98 per cent of the costs of blanket planting could be reclaimed from the public purse. It is no wonder private afforestation began to boom at that time. Since then, however, there has been a steady reduction in the top rates of income tax, down to 60 per cent prior to the 1988 Budget.

Each reduction in tax rate meant that private forestry received less subsidy through tax avoidance, and the forestry lobby began to get distinctly jittery. But the relative attractiveness of afforestation depended on the extent of competition from other tax-avoidance schemes, such as industrial building allowances and equipment leasing, and these were steadily closed by the same government. This meant that despite the decline in the top rate of tax to 60 per cent, private afforestation went on booming.

The forestry lobby began to get anxious before the 1988 Budget when it became obvious that the top rate of tax was to be cut yet again, to unprecedented low levels. The crucial issue was whether forestry investors would still be attracted to tax-avoidance afforestation if the tax rates dropped much further: 'We have seen a steady watering down of tax rates and we are promised a continuation of this policy; a top rate of 50 per cent or less is almost upon us. Will planters continue to pay high prices for scarce FGS-cleared land to obtain 50 per cent tax relief on the Schedule D account? Some will, but a lot won't' (*F&BT* March 1988).

As the Chancellor of the Exchequer rose to make his Budget speech the forestry lobby held its breath . . .

The slide into disrepute

During the 1980s the afforestation industry blundered into a series of crises of its own making. The forestry ploughs dug into the Flow Country, as poorer and poorer quality land was planted. At Crichness and Shielsknowe afforestation went ahead without grants, proposals were submitted to afforest the Creag Meagaidh SSSI, and the Kinnell scandal erupted (see Chapter 9). The public image of the forestry industry went from bad to worse.

From 1986 onwards a series of critical reports from the Ramblers Association, the NCC, the CPRE and the NAO, assailed the afforestation industry. The NAO (1986) report focused attention onto the extremely low rates of return achieved by the FC's planting of poor quality land and suggested that, in real terms, the private sector was unlikely to do any better. The forestry lobby's image was seriously tarnished by the time of the 1988 Budget, and the government felt able to announce major reforms.

The 1988 Budget

The top rate of tax was slashed to 40 per cent, down from 60 per cent, on taxable incomes over £19,300 per year in the 1988 Budget. This alone would have transformed the basis of tax-avoidance afforestation as the cost to a private investor of planting a large block of conifers would have increased to 150 per cent of its former level. The net cost to a typical investor, paying tax at 60 per cent and with a grant under the FGS, of planting 500 acres (200 ha) of land would have soared from £60,000 to £90,000. This would have undoubtedly led to a sharp decline in the number of prospective investors, and could even have led to the collapse of the private afforestation industry.

But the Budget went further, and made speculation about the effects of the tax cuts irrelevant, by wholly removing commercial woodlands from the scope of income tax and corporation tax. This effectively abolished Schedule B, and the application of Schedule D to forestry. Tax avoidance as an incentive for afforestation immediately ceased. Removal from taxation meant that timber sales remained tax free without the need to resort to the archaic artifices of Schedule B.

Forestry's 'big bang' was tempered only by transitional arrangements that allow tax relief to continue until April 1993 for those who were already owners or tenants of commercial woodland. The transitional arrangements also apply to those who became occupiers as a result of commitments entered into, or applications for grants received by the FC, before 15 March 1988.

The FC's Woodland Grant Scheme

Conservation groups may have celebrated the closure of the tax loophole, but the FC's new system of planting grants under the WGS raised the spectre of continued blanket afforestation. The WGS brought in massive rises in the level of conifer planting grants which went up to between 159 and 256 per cent of their former levels under the FGS (Table 6.1). Grant rates for broadleaved planting were raised at the same time.

Table 6.1: *Forestry's 'big bang': the new incentives*

INCENTIVES FOR CONIFER AFFORESTATION			
Before the 1988 Budget –		After the Budget	
1. Tax avoidance		1. FC planting grants for conifers under the Woodland Grant Scheme (WGS)	
2. FC planting grants under the Forestry Grant Scheme (FGS)			
Area approved for planting in hectares	*Rate of grant per hectare*	*Rate of grant per hectare*	*Percentage increase %*
0.25 – 0.9	£630	£1,005	159%
1.0 – 2.9	£505	£ 880	174%
3.0 – 9.9	£420	£ 795	189%
10 and over	£240	£ 615	256%

1 hectare = 2.471 acres

It is most significant that the largest rise took place for the planting of areas over 25 acres (10 ha) which is the grant band that sustains blanket afforestation. With establishment costs of £400 per acre (£1,000 per ha), it is clear that the new grant was designed to cover just over 60 per cent of those costs, which is almost precisely the level of subsidy formerly available through tax avoidance immediately before the Budget. Exactly as under the FGS, the new flat-rate grant remains the same whether 25 acres (10 ha) are planted, or whether 4,000 acres (1,600 ha) are blanketed with conifers. There can be no doubt that the intention is for large-scale, conifer afforestation to continue.

Despite the high level of the new planting grants, the removal of tax avoidance had a traumatic effect on the forestry lobby. This was compounded by the Secretary of State for the Environment's announcement that there would be a presumption against further large-scale, conifer afforestation in the uplands of England. It was left to the Secretaries of State for Wales and Scotland to soothe the anxieties of the forestry lobby, which they attempted to do with statements of continuing support for the afforestation industry, and homage to the annual target of 81,500 acres (33,000 ha) of planting.

Effects of the 'Big Bang' on forestry investors

It is clear that grants under the WGS will provide a similar level of taxpayers' subsidy to upland afforestation to that formerly available though tax-avoidance incentives. Paying the subsidy in the form of grants could theoretically enable a wider spectrum of people to invest in afforestation, including existing landowners and less wealthy individuals, in addition to the small group of 40–60 very wealthy individuals who formerly sought tax avoidance through afforestation each year.

The crucial difference will be in the motivation for planting. Although afforestation will still be a method for investors to convert income into capital, tax avoidance provided a compelling, psychological and financial incentive, which the afforestation industry will sorely miss. The richest people in Britain gained huge benefits from the income tax reductions in the Budget, which will give them greatly increased spending power. Whether they will still choose to plant large-scale forests remains to be seen. Some think the balance of support for the afforestation industry will shift towards farmers and landowners and that: 'Large-scale afforestation of bare land by outside investors may well be a thing of the past. The industry will survive but its structure in the 1990s is likely to be very different' (*F&BT* April 1988).

Effects on the forestry companies

Within a few weeks of the 1988 budget, the forestry companies were beginning their sales pitch to a new range of potential investors. They will certainly miss the steady stream of referrals of top-rate taxpayers which was channelled to them from financial advisers and accountants, often on a commission basis. What were formerly sold as the secondary advantages of afforestation for tax avoidance have immediately been dusted-off and brought to the forefront. Forestry is now hailed as a 'fun' investment, providing personal facilities for sporting and recreation, in a setting that is sold as coming complete with abundant wildlife and attractive scenery. It is likely that the purchase of whole farms will be advocated for conversion into forest estates, with paddocks for grazing livestock, and opportunities for sporting. The concessions available on IHT, and the exemption of tree crops from CGT, will also be highlighted.

There will at least be a welcome end to the rush to buy forestry land in the last weeks of the tax year, and to put trees in the ground before 5 April. In the absence of tax avoidance, and with investors looking more closely at the likely rate of return on their investment, there may well be increasing competition between companies on the costs of their planting contracts. Companies may well have to submit competitive tenders for planting a given forestry scheme. Such trends can only be a healthy development for the industry.

Unfortunately, what will not change is the attraction of very large afforestation contracts. The large contracts will still be the most profitable, and will be pursued with the greatest vigour by the companies. It is likely that pension funds will be the particular target of a sales drive to encourage continued blanket afforestation.

Effects on pension funds

Because they are tax-exempt institutions, pension funds were never able to benefit from tax avoidance to subsidise their forestry operations. Their main contribution to the afforestation industry was as the foundation of the secondary market, as purchasers of established plantations. None the less, some funds, advised by certain of the companies, did carry out bare land afforestation with only the FGS planting grant to reduce their costs. PIEDA (1986) estimated that 10 per cent of Scottish planting was undertaken by such institutions.

Under the FGS, planting grants at about £100 per acre (£240 per ha) would only have accounted for 25 per cent of the costs of a planting scheme by a pension fund. If some funds were prepared to plant on that basis, then there may well be a substantial increase in their planting activities, now that the WGS grants are sufficient to cover 60 per cent of the costs of planting a large area of conifers. The new grants are quite sufficient to allow pension funds to achieve the return of 4 to 6 per cent that they are seeking on their forestry investments. So far, forestry interests have maintained a discreet silence about the future role of pension funds. But as Bond (1988) reports: 'Fountain Forestry remains quietly optimistic about the future of planting in general (after all it has two large pension fund clients planting in the Flows, which as gross funds do not receive tax relief)'.

It is also likely that the switch from tax avoidance to planting grants will force considerable reductions in charges made by the afforestation companies for carrying out large-scale planting contracts. Their clients will be much more cost-conscious without the cushion of tax avoidance. As planting costs fall, the grants will cover a greater proportion of those costs, which will be a major new incentive for blanket afforestation.

It is a matter of great concern to conservationists that the pension funds, advised by the forestry companies, may well become the driving force behind continued blanket planting. Their preference for the large-scale, monocultural, conifer plantations that characterise upland afforestation is already obvious. The total extent of the 1987/88 afforestation market, consisting of £15–20 million worth of planting contracts, could easily be absorbed by the vast financial resources of the pension funds.

Effects on the forestry land price

The revolution in forestry finances will have a major effect on land prices, as the decisions of a new mix of investment interests begin to shape a fresh market for forestry land. It will be some time before the new marketing strategies of the forestry companies take full effect, and their results can be seen. Under Schedule D, income tax relief was allowed on the payments of interest on loans to buy forestry land. The cessation of this alone is likely to bring land prices tumbling down, even though the cost of afforestation is still going to be subsidised at close to its former levels.

Several of the forestry companies have indicated that they think the price of land with forestry clearance will drop from £300 per acre (£750 per ha) down to £150–200 per acre (£370–500 per ha). Such reductions would clearly affect the volume of sales of farming land being sold for forestry, by reducing the price differential between the two. In some areas of hill land it is likely that the forestry price will closely match the farming price at the above levels. However, in the absence of a particularly active market for such land between farmers, land may well still sell for forestry, simply because there is no real alternative. There will always be a number of forced sales with some farmers having to sell land to raise capital.

In theory, the new grant incentives should encourage a more rational appraisal of afforestation as an investment, in terms of the potential rate of return. This in turn should mean that better quality land is planted, but this will not necessarily be the case. The highest differential between farming and forestry land prices is likely to be maintained on the very poorest farm land. In the Flow Country, for example, land worth £10 per acre (£25 per ha) for farming could formerly be sold for forestry for £100 per acre (£250 per ha). Similar differentials operated on the Island of Islay. The ten-fold increase could be much reduced without impairing the pressure on landowners to sell for afforestation.

The afforestation industry is still likely to be dependent on planting very large schemes. The forestry companies will continue to find planting large contracts their most profitable activity, and pension funds will always want to buy great tracts of plantation. Although the uncertainties in the market may create a short-term reduction in planting activity, it seems inevitable that blanket afforestation will gradually build up to its former levels, with all of the problems that are entailed for wildlife and landscape in the uplands. Indeed, it is government policy that planting should expand dramatically to reach the 81,500 acre (33,000 ha) target, and it is clear that this is going to be a major feature of the forestry lobby's future campaigning.

Effects on the FC

The good news for the FC is that it will be able to regain some power to influence afforestation schemes. No longer will it be possible for investors to plant large blocks of conifers without grants, ignoring the voluntary consultation process, but getting the benefit of full tax avoidance.

The bad news for the FC is that subsidies paid by planting grants will become clearly visible in its accounts, and will no longer be completely invisible as tax avoidance. All eyes will become focused on the FC as the paymaster behind the upland afforestation that seems set to continue as before. There will be the opportunity to put the FC under much greater pressure to explain why it is continuing to subsidise the afforestation of poor quality land, some of which is already approved for forestry in the secret land banks. The element of grant-in-aid to the Forestry Authority needed to sustain upland conifer planting, is likely to rise from about £5 million per year to over £11 million per year if current planting levels are maintained. If the 81,500 acre (33,000 ha) target is ever actually met, then a total of around £20 million of grants is likely to be needed each year. Any grants to encourage lowland planting under the Farm Woodlands Scheme (FWS) will be in addition to this.

The change to planting grants will also be seen by the FC as an ominous precursor to complete privatisation, as they provide a more sane, quantifiable, and controllable basis for the future running of a completely privatised industry.

= 7 =

The Privatisation of Forestry

The privatisation of planting

The major change in the pattern of blanket afforestation since 1980 has been its discreet privatisation by the Conservative government. During 1985/86 private sector afforestation spread across almost 47,000 acres (19,019 ha) of land. Over the same period the FC purchased a mere 2,310 acres (935 ha) of land for new planting, but it also sold off a slightly larger area of 2,528 acres (1,023 ha) of planting land, so that it actually suffered a net loss. Only by using up its reserve of land acquired in previous years was the FC able to keep planting. It planted 10,707 acres (4,333 ha) from its reserve in 1985/86, and had a further 75,000 acres (30,000 ha) in hand. A forlorn statement in the 1985/86 Annual Report notes that the FC's main reserve of land in the north of Scotland will run out in five or six years. The dramatic decline in the fortunes of FC planting in Scotland, the centre of the afforestation industry, is shown in Figure 7.1.

The switch to private sector afforestation has been the ideological whim of the government, but the FC has also been a victim of the land price spiral. In 1960 the FC paid under £4 per acre (£9 per ha) for planting land, but by 1978 the average was £66 per acre (£164 per ha), and this had soared to £119 per acre (£295 per ha) in 1979. The FC never really stood a chance. As a publicly-owned Forestry Enterprise it had to compete on the open market for the purchase of forestry land with a private sector subsidised to the hilt by tax avoidance. At the same time the Forestry Authority paid out the planting grants, which together with competition between the afforestation companies, pushed the price of planting land out of reach of the Forestry Enterprise.

Selling off the Forestry Commission

Morale in the FC is currently low. This is partly due to a messy reorganisation from four-tier to three-tier management, but mainly stems from the first steps towards what may become full-scale privatisation. The privatisation of the process of land acquisition and afforestation, which has halted the expansion of the FC estate,

76

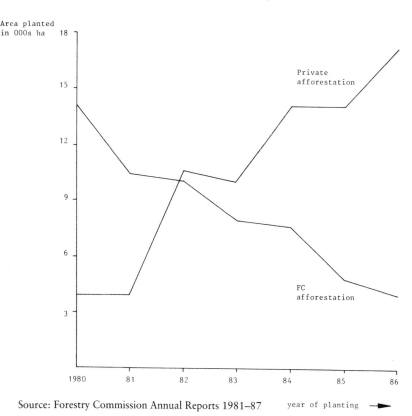

Source: Forestry Commission Annual Reports 1981–87   year of planting ➤

Figure 7.1 *The decline of Forestry Commission planting in Scotland*

is described above. This in itself is an affront to foresters who have devoted their careers to the holy crusade of a target area of land to be planted. The second facet of privatisation which has had a more direct impact on the FC is the sale of land and plantations owned by the FC to the private sector. This disposals programme was announced in the Forestry Act of 1981 with the aim of reducing the FC's call on Exchequer funds. The original plan was to raise £40 million over three years but the target was gradually raised to £100 million over eight years. In November 1984 the main purpose was revised to rationalising the estate and improving the efficiency and commercial effectiveness of the Forestry Enterprise.

Much of the speculation about FC properties being sold off cheaply is misplaced, and represents a misunderstanding of the private sector market where plantation prices are low in relation to the cost of establishing them, and low in comparison with bare land prices. The view of the NAO (1986) was that the sales have no adverse consequences for the FC or the Exchequer as long as future income and expenditure flows are used to determine reserve prices. It is, of course, normal to set an asking price which is higher than the reserve, so that a sale can still be successful if the full asking price is not achieved.

The FC soon found that only a limited number of institutions were active in the forestry market: 'We were lucky if we got four or five enquiries for most of the sales. Sometimes we only got one and we were pleased to get that' (*Glasgow Herald* 16 July 1985). The number of institutions bidding for a plantation is often a reflection of the fact that there are four major afforestation companies, each advising a separate institutional client.

The secret sales

The sales of public assets into the secretive world of forestry invest-ment have naturally generated criticism, not least from the PAC. Despite intensive questioning the government has refused to give details of the purchasers of FC assets on the grounds of commercial confidence. But following the PAC investigations in 1985 the FC has approached purchasers to seek consent to the disclosure of information about the sales, although less than half of the pur-chasers involved consented to a full disclosure. The FC realised that: 'The big institutions just don't like their business made public . . . It doesn't take much to scare them away' (*Glasgow Herald* 16 July 1985).

In fact a wide range of purchasers have been involved, including a private individual who paid £1.65 million for the FC's Raera Forest, and the pension fund of the European Organisation for Nuclear Research which paid £1 million for the Leithope Forest.

Benefits to the public?

The question of whether the public benefits in the long-term from the transfer of virtually all new afforestation to the private sector is a matter for debate. Any benefits to the wider economy in terms of timber production and job creation are similar whether the planting is done by the FC or private interests, with the comparative merits depending only on relative efficiency as noted by the NAO (1986).

A clear casualty of the extension of private forestry, however, is public access. FC forests are indelibly associated in the public mind with freedom of access. The FC uses this fact to control access to woodlands. If it does not put an FC sign outside one of its wood-lands then people assume it is privately owned and are discouraged from entering. The FC also provides at least a token recreational resource of car parks, campsites and marked walks, although the recreational potential of the bulk of its upland Sitka plantations is severely limited. Few people would be foolhardy enough to stray from a marked walk into a thicket of the sharp-needled conifers.

The private sector in general harbours a carefully disguised antipathy to public access (Shoard 1987). This is part of ingrained attitudes to land ownership in Britain and not just a response to slightly increased risks of fire damage and vandalism which are no greater than in FC plantations. EFG (1985a) in its brochure deals with 'conservation and amenity forestry' but the approach does not seem orientated towards the general public: 'Some famous names find their forests the only places where they can get complete privacy and seclusion and many people buy properties in the Home Counties simply to be able to walk through them with the family.'

The NAO (1986) concluded that the incentives available to private planting could only be justified if there were social benefits, such as the provision of employment or recreational benefits, not reflected in the commercial returns. With considerable understatement it found that such benefits 'appear if anything to be less in the private than the public sector'.

The future for privatisation

Political in-fighting over further privatisation of the FC is, no doubt, continuing. An offer for the purchase of the whole of the FC is thought to have already been made by a major oil company. Reports indicate that the Secretary of State for Scotland has been influential in arguing against wholesale privatisation. He must be well aware that the FC owns or leases 10 per cent of Scotland, and the most likely purchasers would be individuals and institutions based firmly in England. The whole issue of privatisation is likely to resurface in 1989 when the current programme of FC disposals is completed. It remains to be seen if the government would be so unkind as to sell the FC on its seventieth anniversary. A trend towards privatisation can be noted from the pressure which the FC is putting upon its workers to give up their employed status and become contractors. This is being encouraged by reducing their opportunities to supplement their low basic wages by piece-work.

= 8 =
The Forestry Lobby –
the Fifty

There is a range of overlapping memberships amongst the various groups that make up the forestry lobby, which disguises the fact that it has as its core a mere 150 people. Senior staff at the Forestry Commission are active and number about 15 individuals. Sawmilling and timber processing industries field about ten prominent representatives. The higher echelons of the afforestation companies expend a great deal of effort in lobbying, and there are probably about ten key campaigners. There is also a group of perhaps five academics from the forestry universities. The real heart of the forestry lobby lies with the major landowners. They fill the ranks of the TGUK and the CLA, and sit on the Regional Advisory Committees (RACs). Overall, the forestry lobby can be seen to consist of just 50 most conspicuous activists. It is this tiny group of people which does most to determine the course of British forestry.

It must be stressed that lobbying is a normal and perfectly legitimate activity in the pursuit of an interest in a democratic society, and members of the forestry lobby must be admired for their enthusiasm and commitment. Lobbying is only open to criticism if it makes really unfair use of privileged positions, sustains untenable arguments, or exploits undue advantages over others who represent different interests.

The Forestry Commission

The FC has the legal status and functions of a government department. It reports directly to the Forestry Ministers, who are the Minister of Agriculture and the Secretaries of State for Wales and Scotland. Because 60 per cent of all FC plantations are in Scotland, and 90 per cent of afforestation takes place there, the Secretary of State for Scotland is the chief Forestry Minister.

The most striking feature of the FC's organisation is the unique way that it allows private forestry to argue its case at the heart of the government machine. Unlike other departments of state, the FC is not run entirely by officials subject to the appointment procedures applied to all civil servants.

The FC chairmen

The chairman of the FC is, by tradition, a landowner himself. Indeed, it was totally fitting that the trees that began the blanket afforestation of the uplands were planted on a hillside near Elgin in Scotland by the 16th Lord Lovat, the first chairman, soon after the creation of the FC in November 1919. Hours earlier, Lord Clinton, a Forestry Commissioner who went on to become the second chairman, had planted trees at Eggesford Forest in Devon. Over the next 70 years a succession of lords and landowners have dominated the chairmanship of the FC.

The Forestry Commissioners

The FC chairman heads a board of ten other Forestry Commissioners. Three Commissioners are career FC staff, led by the director-general, and a fourth is an outside civil servant, all of whom are full-time executives. The remaining six, part-time Commissioners are appointed for their knowledge and experience of the timber trade, forestry, trade union matters, the countryside, the forestry and wood processing industries, and outside industries.

The representation of trade union interests is not those of forestry workers or foresters, and this appointment is currently held by the general secretary of the Scottish Teachers Union. Of the other current Commissioners one is managing director of a firm of timber importers; another is a member of the Audit Commission and the Eastern Electricity Board; and one is a vice-chairman of Tate & Lyle and former financial director of Cadbury Schweppes. The remaining two part-time Commissioner posts are occupied by representatives from the TGUK, one from England or Wales, and one from Scotland.

As will be shown below, the TGUK is a small pressure group, formed to preserve the interests of forestry and landowners. To find its representatives amongst the top echelons of the FC is a clear indication of its power and influence. By contrast, members of the much larger pressure group, Friends of the Earth, are not yet routinely appointed to influential positions in official environmental agencies such as the NCC or the Countryside Commission.

The FC Advisory Committees

Private forestry interests are heavily represented on the other committees that advise the Forestry Commissioners. The main statutory committee is the Home Grown Timber Advisory

Committee (HGTAC), set up under the 1951 Forestry Act. No fewer than 18 of the 25 members of the committee are currently drawn from nominations by the TGUK and timber using industries. The remaining members are appointed by the Commissioners after consultation with organisations which seem to them to represent the interests of woodland owners. The Forestry Commissioners are also advised by the three National Advisory Committees (NACs) for England, Scotland and Wales, which are composed of the chairmen of the RACs.

The Regional Advisory Committees

The FC divides Britain up into seven administrative regions or Conservancies, and there is an RAC for each one. The eight or nine members of each RAC are selected by the FC, with four of them, and often the chairman as well, representing forestry interests, so that there is an unrepentant forestry bias. The remaining four members are chosen by the FC to represent agriculture, the environment, trade-unions and planning.

Every year the list of members in the FC Annual Report reads like a roll call of the forestry lobby. So discredited had the lack of impartiality of the RACs become by early 1988 that the FC was forced into announcing that their chairmen will now be selected to ensure that there is 'unlikely to be a clash of interest when disputed cases are considered by their committee' (*F&BT* February 1988). It is unlikely that this token gesture will do anything to restore credibility. The controversial role of the RACs, where the battle for the hills is fought, is explained in Chapter 9.

The partnership between state and private sectors

As Forestry Authority, the FC advises the government on forestry policy and supports and encourages private forestry. At the same time it exercises *de facto* control over the supply of planting land which concerns the private sector and its own Forestry Enterprise:

'The responsibilities of the director of land-use planning have been enlarged to include aspects of private forestry. Collaboration with and assistance to private forestry is an increasingly important part of our work and this change will help discharge that task more effectively. The director will continue his predecessor's responsibility for land-use planning questions including the transfer of land from agriculture and other uses to forestry, which are very closely linked with our work on private forestry matters and with our own afforestation programme' (*F&BT* May 1978).

Similarly, the FC foresaw no change 'in the present policy that state and private forestry should go hand in hand with new afforestation . . . the key to this for both of us is the continued availability of plantable land which is a diminishing resource . . . for both state and private sectors it is essential to make the case for further afforestation' (*F&BT* January 1979).

The common objective of continued afforestation concerns both state and private sectors and the resulting partnership has ensured support from both major political parties and allowed the survival of the afforestation industry for 60 years. When a Conservative government is in power it praises and promotes the contribution of the private sector. A Labour government is heartened by a state-owned, wood-production industry, and when taxes were increased, private afforestation for tax avoidance was inadvertently made more attractive.

The forestry lobby stresses how well the partnership works: 'Forestry is the perfect example of a mixed economy in action' (*F&BT* February 1978). The threat of privatisation hanging over the FC, ironically, is a danger to the partnership that is only too apparent. The FC hoped:

'that nothing will disrupt the present partnership between public and private interests . . . There has been acceptance by successive governments of the importance of forestry and of the need for a stable long-term policy in both public and private sectors. Having said that, all public-sector expenditure is currently under review and the Commission's finance is no exception' (*F&BT* August 1979).

Private sector foresters have criticised the sale of FC assets and the cutback in FC planting. A spokesman for Tilhill Forestry is reported as saying: 'The industry as a whole was not completely in favour of the sales programme.' He suggested that it did not create any new acres of forest and said he would prefer to see the money obtained ploughed back into the forestry kitty (*F&BT* July 1984). EFG seems to regret the decline in FC planting: 'Sadly the Forestry Commission were relieved of all income from disposals by the Treasury rather than leaving funds for continued planting' (1986c).

The president of the Institute of Foresters (now the Institute of Chartered Foresters) was reported to have similar views:

'However, the IoF expressed "grave reservations" (pending clarification) on proposals for selling some of the Forestry Commission's forests to private interests. The president feared for harmful effects on the balance established over the past 30 years between state and private sectors and said that sale proceeds should only be used for expansion of the forest industry' (*F&BT* February 1981).

So successful has the lobby been in promoting the idea of a partnership that reassurances have been given on behalf of a Conservative government dedicated to privatisation: 'It is not our intention to dissolve the successful partnership between the FC and private woodland interests, but we shall certainly wish to see a more significant private sector investment than has been the case in the past' (*F&BT* June 1980).

The links between state and private sector are also shown by the appointment of senior FC staff to the afforestation companies on their retirement (Table 8.1) and Grove (1983) quotes Lord Taylor of Gryfe:

'The great thing about forestry is that it is a partnership. The dreary debates between public and private sectors which bedevil other areas of our national economic life do not apply to the rational world of men and women who grow trees. It was therefore an easy transition when I ceased to be chairman of the FC and became chairman of the Economic Forestry Group.'

Table 8.1: *Appointment of senior Forestry Commission staff and politicians by the forestry companies*

Lord Taylor of Gryfe	FC chairman	EFG chairman
John Dickson	FC director-general	EFG director, Forest Thinnings director
Dallas Mithen	Forestry Commissioner	Tilhill director
Earl Ferrers	Minister of State MAFF, Conservative Deputy Leader in the House of Lords	EFG director
Lord Rees	Chief Secretary to the Treasury 1983–85, EFG woodland owner	EFG chairman
Sir Jasper More	Former MP for Ludlow, chairman of Conservative Party Parliamentary Forestry Sub-Committee	Flintshire Woodlands president

The landowners

The forestry land price spiral has been a hindrance to some sectors of the afforestation industry, but landowners who have been able to sell land for afforestation have benefited. In order to protect the privileges of land ownership, such as the creation and preservation of wealth, landowners have formed three pressure groups. The Scottish Landowners' Federation (SLF) protects the interests of landowners in Scotland, and the CLA performs the same function in England and Wales. The TGUK itself was formed as an offshoot of the CLA. Because of the narrow base of land ownership these pressure groups can never be large organisations, with the CLA boasting about 44,000 members, and the TGUK just over 2,500. However, these lobbies are most influential.

An understanding of the pattern of land ownership is essential to an appreciation of the forestry lobby, but investigation is not welcomed, as 'Silvestris' has noted: 'You do not have to be left-wing, or anti-landlord or envious to be curious. But just mention the subject and you get branded by the Scottish establishment as left-wing, or anti-landlord, or envious; if you are lucky enough, all three at once' (*F&BT* January 1978).

Similarly a Conservative Shadow Minister of Agriculture, addressing the TGO annual general meeting, stressed the danger of making forestry appear to be a 'tax-haven' that would invite the attentions of the 'envious and malevolent' (*F&BT* March 1978).

A striking feature of land ownership in Britain is its concentration into only a few hands. The richest 1 per cent of the population owns 52 per cent of all personally-owned land. A further 22 per cent of such land is owned by the next most wealthy group which makes up just 2 to 5 per cent of the population (Royal Commission 1979). Land ownership in Scotland is especially heavily concentrated, and this is particularly important as the vast majority of afforestation is taking place there. Robin Callander (1987) shows that this pattern has been maintained for over a century. In the 1870s nearly 60 per cent of Scotland was held in estates of over 20,000 acres (8,000 ha). Nowadays there are still 1,700 estates larger than 1,000 acres (400 ha) which account for three-quarters of all the privately-owned land. Half of all private land is owned by less than 600 estates each with 5,000 acres (2,000 ha) or more, giving Scotland a more concentrated pattern of private land ownership than any other country in Europe.

A milestone in the search for an understanding of Scottish land-ownership was achieved by John McEwen (1981), when he listed the top 100 landowners. The top ten landowners are shown in

Table 8.2, together with others from the top 100. Some of the names are instantly recognisable as influential and enthusiastic foresters.

Table 8.2: *Scotland's landowning elite*

The top ten landowners –

Owner	Estate	Acres*
The Duke of Buccleuch and and Queensberry	Buccleuch Estates	277,000
The Wills family	Wills Estates	263,000
The Earl of Seafield	Seafield Estates	185,000
The Countess of Sutherland	Sutherland Estates	158,000
The Duke of Atholl	Atholl Estates	130,000
Capt. A.A. Farquharson	Invercauld Estates	119,000
The Duke of Westminster	Westminster Estates	113,000
British Aluminium Ltd	British Aluminium Estates	110,000
The Earl of Stair	Stair Estates	110,000
Sir Donald Cameron of Lochiel	Lochiel Estates	98,000

Other landowners from the top 100 –

Owner	Estate	Acres*
The Duke of Roxburghe	Roxburgh Estates	96,000
Brigadier, The Lord Lovat	Lovat Estates	76,000
The Duke of Argyll	Argyll Estates	74,000
The Lord Home of The Hirsel	Douglas Home Estates	54,000
The Earl of Mansfield	Scone	41,000
The Lord Burton	Dochfour Estates	39,000
The Earl Cawdor	Cawdor Estates	39,000
H.M. The Queen	Balmoral Estates	35,000
A.B.L. Munro-Ferguson	Novar Estates	34,000
Mr and Mrs Balfour	Balbirnie and Scourie	25,000

1 acre = 0.4 hectare
Source: McEwen (1981)

The Timber Growers United Kingdom

Despite being a tiny, minority pressure group, the TGUK has done much to preserve the afforestation industry in the face of sustained criticism. From its base amongst the landowning establishment it now co-ordinates all the elements of the forestry lobby. The origins of the TGUK go back to the formation of the TGO, as an offshoot of the CLA, in 1959. A merger with the Timber Growers Scotland (TGS), itself the successor to the Scottish Woodland Owners Association (SWOA), created the TGUK in 1983.

The evolution of the timber growers lobby is an interesting reflection of the development of the afforestation industry. When the TGO was formed there was a rush to join, with 90 per cent of the maximum membership total reached in the first few years. This early membership was concentrated amongst the owners of traditional, estate woodlands, which are characterised by small or medium sized blocks of woodland, probably forming part of a larger, mixed estate. Membership peaked at 1,887 members in 1966 and declined steadily thereafter. At the time of the formation of the TGUK there were only 1,443 ordinary members of the TGO, to merge with the 1,211 members of the TGS (Figure 8.1). At its inception in 1983 the TGUK could muster only 2,654 members.

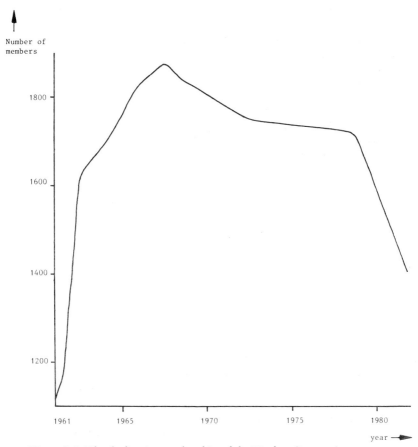

Figure 8.1 *The decline in membership of the Timber Growers' Organisation*   Source: *Timber Grower* Magazine

The declining membership of the TGO was due to the steady loss from its ranks of the owners of smaller woodlands. This was reported at the 17th annual general meeting in 1978: 'The majority of resignations attributable directly to the subscription increase occurred amongst the owners of the smaller woodland holdings.' This is understandable in view of the high cost of TGUK membership. In England and Wales the base rate was £20 per annum in 1987, increasing with the area owned up to a maximum of £995 for holdings of 3,755 acres (1,520 ha) or more. In Scotland the maximum subscription is £620.

As small-scale woodlands make a great contribution to the remaining beauty of the countryside, and to its wildlife, it is a pity that their owners have steadily lost their influence in the forestry lobby. This unfortunate process has been matched by the growing power of the interests behind blanket planting of conifers – the afforestation companies and their clients – a fact that was noted at the 12th annual general meeting of the TGO in 1973: 'In recent years, however, such net increases in membership as there have been, have been largely attributable to new woodland owners introduced by the leading forestry investment companies.' Such owners, of course, tend to own large plantations and generate a healthy subscription income for the TGUK.

At the time of the merger, TGS members owned just over 500,000 acres (200,000 ha) of forest, with an average size of ownership of 426 acres (173 ha). Figures from 1979 indicated that TGO members owned a similar total area of forest in England and Wales, but the average size of ownership was much less at 288 acres (116 ha). These average figures disguise the fact that a few major forestry investors amongst TGUK members own a vast area of plantations (as shown in Figure 8.2). The decline in the number of members owning smaller woodlands is shown by the fact that in 1968 about 75 per cent of TGO members owned less than 250 acres (100 ha) of woodland, but in 1986 this had reduced to 65 per cent of TGUK members owning less than this amount.

The forestry lords

It was observed in the *EFG Magazine* (1986c) that: 'The Lords have always taken a kindly, expert interest in forestry.' Nothing else could be expected in the light of their plethora of landowning, forestry and business interests. The House of Lords is the heart of the forestry lobby.

There has been no full-scale forestry debate in the House of Commons since 1945, only a few, short adjournment debates. By

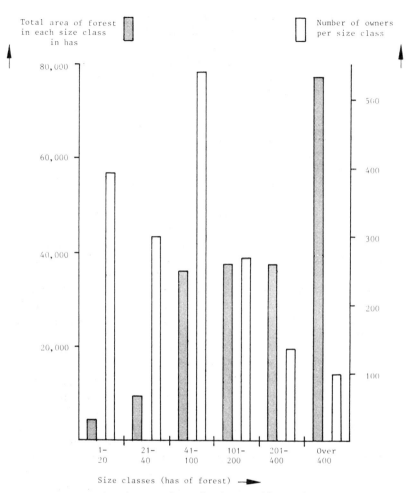

Figure 8.2 *Size distribution of woodlands owned by Timber Growers' Organisation members in 1979*   Source: Timber Growers' Organisation 1980

contrast, the Lords debated forestry extensively in 1973, 1976, 1978 and 1988. Summing up the 1973 debate it was noted that three-quarters of the speeches came from speakers who had experience of forestry or who were established in Scotland (*F&BT* October/November 1973).

The House of Lords boasts an array of ardent foresters, and with a panoply of landowning interests, ensures a permanent, inbuilt majority for the forestry lobby. It is apt that the less frequent attenders at the House of Lords are known as the 'backwoods' peers.

The afforestation companies

By expanding the area of land under blanket afforestation, the forestry companies form the foundation of the afforestation industry. Because their activities are so heavily dependent on public subsidy and the goodwill of the government, they are expert advocates of the forestry cause. One of the most spectacular manifestations of EFG's campaigning in action is its annual luncheon. This usually involves the leading members of the FC, past and present, together with government ministers, landowners and shareholders. Landowners are also associated with the companies and are often appointed as directors.

The foresters

The foresters' main professional body is the Institute of Chartered Foresters (ICF, formerly the IoF), which sets out to maintain and improve standards of forestry practice, and to spread and to promote all aspects of forestry. Its limited 1987 membership of 137 Fellows and 570 Ordinary members, reflects the small size of Britain's forestry industry.

Senior FC staff and private sector foresters mingle in the ranks of the ICF, together with a seasoning of forestry academics, and the overlapping memberships of the forestry world are clearly illustrated. Past presidents of the ICF include forestry academics, Forestry Commissioners, and the directors of forestry companies. The governing council of the ICF has 15 members with a strong representation of private sector forestry interests.

The other main foresters' organisation is the Association of Professional Foresters (APF). There are also the two forestry societies – The Royal Forestry Society (RFS) of England, Wales and Northern Ireland, and the Royal Scottish Forestry Society (RSFS). These help to consolidate contacts between landowners, forest owners, foresters and the forestry companies.

The forestry academics

The forestry academics played a major role in the production of the 1980 CAS Report, which advocated a massive increase in afforestation throughout Britain, with National Parks expected to take their full share. They were also largely responsible for *Afforestation and Nature Conservation: Interactions* (1986), a bid by the TGUK to counter a critical report by the NCC in 1986.

The four main universities with forestry interests are Aberdeen,

Bangor, Edinburgh and Oxford. Professor Matthews has pointed out that Aberdeen University has been closely associated with private forestry in Scotland for more than 25 years: 'We watched with admiration the remarkable progress of new planting during the 1960s and early seventies and shared in the disappointment, frustration and uncertainty that followed the review of forest policy in 1972' (*F&BT* August/September 1978). Also from Aberdeen University, Professor Miller (1985) wrote that: 'In confessing to being a forester I have a deep and vested interest in the continued health of Britain's forest estate for upon it depends the future of my profession and the employment prospects of my students.'

The politicians

Politicians who have been appointed onto the boards of forestry companies are shown in Table 8.1. Strong overlaps between land and forest ownership, and political activity are widely apparent in Britain. The arrival of two new Conservative MPs at Westminster in 1979 was warmly greeted by the forestry lobby: 'It is good to see that the industry has such advocates at Westminster' (*F&BT* August 1979). Both MPs represented Scottish constituencies and had published booklets promoting forestry.

Links into the financial establishment

Every year that goes by allows the afforestation industry to entrench its position. At the same time the network of financial links becomes more complex, as pension funds, banks, timber merchants and forestry companies expand their businesses and become more deeply committed. Tax and finance experts are frequently appointed to the boards of forestry companies. The development of the forestry industry can only make the task of conservationists, to change the course of forestry, progressively more difficult.

Forestry links into environmental organisations

Ogilvy (1986) is clear about the centre of opposition to blanket afforestation: 'It should be noted that both the NCC and the RSPB are opposed to further upland afforestation, and, with the support of nervous politicians, they present the most significant threat to major expansion.' The forestry lobby has extensive links, aided by landowning connections, into environmental organisations. The NCC itself has a long history of landowning and forestry interests associated with it, as have the Countryside Commissions.

Figure 8.3 *Blanket afforestation at Corlae Plantation. This land, near Carsphairn in south Scotland, was purchased as part of an estate for just £25,000. After afforestation, the plantation was sold to the W.H. Smith pension fund for £761,000 in 1983*

The Forestry Industry Committee Great Britain

For much of the time the forestry lobby appears to be occupied in a game of musical chairs. When a crisis occurs, and the music stops, there is a remarkably speedy and effective concentration on the immediate problem at hand. If only conservation groups could muster the same cohesion and powerbase, and stop sniping at the forestry lobby from their individual positions in an almost competitive manner, then real hope of change in forestry policy might be achieved.

The sight of all the elements of the forestry world forming up for the battle to defend their interests is indeed impressive, even though most of the effect is achieved by a stage army of interlinked organisations that have widely overlapping memberships. The lobby first organised to form the FCGB in the early-1970s, when the cosy, subsidised world of afforestation was threatened by the highly critical Treasury Review.

The TGO's *Timber Grower* (1972) reacted to the Review in splendid style, reporting that private forestry had been plunged 'into its greatest crisis for a generation . . .', by 'a Government which has clearly allowed its fashionable preoccupation with the environment to blind it . . .' But upper lips were stiffened, for woodland owners were 'surely fortunate in having, as their elected representatives at this time, men of great experience, breadth of vision and far-sightedness . . . In such cases the elected few, on spying a spot of light at the end of the tunnel, must lead the many they represent resolutely towards it.'

Further vigorous lobbying was also needed to modify the CTT proposals which created a further threat to forestry during the 1970s. By 1978 the lobby had succeeded in altering the tax greatly, and had recovered a great deal of its composure, enabling it to state of Chancellor Denis Healey: 'It is heartening to see that he has learned the error of his ways, thanks partly to powerful lobbying' (*F&BT* January 1978).

Further proof that it is an attack on its economic credibility that galvanises the forestry world, came after the publication of the highly critical NAO report of 1986. Once again the lobby regrouped, this time into the Forestry Industry Committee of Great Britain (FICGB), in 'one of the most significant public-relations exercises ever undertaken by the industry' (*F&BT* February 1987). The Committee's main aim is to camouflage the drive for blanket afforestation as an essential part of a wider forestry-industrial complex.

The stage army forming the FICGB is shown in Table 8.3. The lobby has no shortage of money for its campaign, with the TGUK drawing £25,000 from its investments to contribute to a first year budget of £120,000.

The mind of the forestry lobby

The great expansion of upland, blanket afforestation has occurred within just one or two working generations of British foresters, and many senior foresters working for afforestation companies have been with them since their inception. It is not to be expected that career foresters who have spent their lives working for the afforestation cause will be able to alter their views overnight, and they are also the inheritors of a tradition of British plantation forestry that goes back to the formation of Wilhelm Schlich's forestry school in 1885. Here a first generation of British foresters grew up in the German and Indian experience of plantation forestry. The French school of forestry with its emphasis on the guidance of natural processes was sadly ignored (Stewart 1987). One of the EFG directors was reported (Grove 1983) to be a retired Indian Forest Service Commissioner who was used to 'talking in square miles in India'.

Table 8.3: *A stage army – the Forestry Industry Committee of Great Britain 1987*

Institutions

TGUK	– Timber Growers UK
ICF	– Institute of Chartered Foresters
APF	– Association of Professional Foresters
RFS	– Royal Forestry Society (E, W & NI)
RSFS	– Royal Scottish Forestry Society
RICS	– Royal Institution of Chartered Surveyors
FTC	– Forestry Training Council
TGWU	– Agricultural and Allied Workers Group Union
Edinburgh University	– Department of Forestry and Natural Resources
Aberdeen University	– Department of Forestry
BTMA	– British Timber Merchants' Association
HTMAS	– Home Timber Merchants' Association Scotland

United Kingdom and Ireland Particleboard Association
British Paper and Board Industry Federation
Forestry Section of the Horticultural Trades Association
Scottish Council for Development and Industry

Corporate

EFG	– forestry companies
Fountain Forestry	
Tilhill	
Scottish Woodlands	
John Clegg & Co	– forestry surveyors and valuers
Bidwells	– land agency firms
Humberts	
Lowther Scott Harden	
Savills	
Woosnam & Tyler	
Aaronson Bros	– timber using industries
Caberboard	
Highland Forest Products	
Shotton Paper	
St Regis Paper (UK)	
Thames Board	
Western Softwoods	

A striking feature of Britain's foresters is their deep conviction that the type of afforestation that they are carrying out is a wholly just crusade of self-evident importance, and that opposition from the public, planners and conservationists is misguided and even malevolent. Foresters seem to pursue their cause with an almost religious intensity, and their faith and conviction only seem to be consolidated by the intense public criticism that the afforestation industry has endured. It seems that the forestry lobby has learned to live with, and even scorn, public hostility.

The attitudes of the forestry lobby bear a striking resemblance to the six symptoms of 'group-think', which have been found to characterise the political decisions made by interest groups (Janis 1972). The following symptoms should be borne in mind when dealing with the forestry lobby:

1. an illusion of invulnerability that becomes shared by most members of the group;
2. collective attempts to ignore or rationalise away items of information challenging shaky but cherished assumptions;
3. an unquestioned belief in the group's inherent morality;
4. stereotyping the enemy as either too evil for negotiations or too stupid to be a threat;
5. self-appointed 'mind-guards' to protect the group from adverse information;
6. a shared illusion of unanimity in a majority viewpoint.

On a lighter note, many foresters' Christmas festivities in 1977 were doubtless cheered by the receipt of Christmas cards bearing messages such as: 'Help generate employment by investing in British forestry', 'self-sufficiency must be improved', 'the UK imports 92 per cent of her forest products' and 'North sea oil will be exhausted by end-century' (*F&BT* November/December 1977). At least the production of the cards will have boosted the wood-pulp industry.

= 9 =

The Battle for the Hills

The balance of power

Both forestry and agriculture are exempt from planning control. Although planning permission is needed to build a small extension to a house, the planting of thousands of acres of land with Sitka spruce is not classed as a 'development' for planning purposes. This anomaly goes back to the 1947 Town and Country Planning Act. In those far-off days, when horses still pulled ploughs, it was never envisaged that the countryside would need to be protected from farming and forestry.

The forestry lobby is vigorously opposed to the extension of planning control to forestry, as shown by its hostility to the Countryside Bill: 'Timber growers are deeply concerned that the bureaucratic controls which it introduces could result in lost home-grown timber production. Planners must not be let loose in the countryside . . .' (*F&BT* February 1981). The TGUK thought that: 'Planning control is primarily negative and often political in character: disputed decisions are reached more by the exhaustion of the parties than by the exercise of quick, clear, logical expertise' (*F&BT* August 1984).

The control of the nature and location of afforestation has been the subject of a bitter, draining battle between the forestry lobby and environmentalists for many years. The lobby is deeply concerned to maintain the role of the Forestry Authority, whilst environmentalists have sought to increase the influence of planners, conservationists, and other land-uses such as farming and recreation, in order to create improved forestry schemes with a wider range of benefits. The whole battle has been over the balance of power in the countryside, and has led to grudging concessions from the forestry lobby and gradual, limited improvements in the FC grant schemes. But this is an exhausting method of dealing with land-use decisions and leads to foresters being cast as destructive of the environment and conservationists as opposing change and always negative.

The difficulties were recognised by J. Clegg & Co in their *Forestry Review of 1985* (1986):

'The whole consultative procedure invites immediate reform, but within a strategy for upland land-use which recognises economic realities. There is no sign of this from either the agricultural or forestry interests, and a major collison now seems unavoidable ... We do foresee a bitter and unrewarding conflict of the many interests in land-use planning, to the detriment of the development of our industry.'

The NCC thinks that some greater degree of regulation of new planting is necessary, and contrasts this with government policy of minimising controls and encouraging voluntary solutions to the problems. In the view of the NCC (1986): 'The present *laissez-faire* is an archaic and unsatisfactory approach which heightens conflict instead of reducing it.'

The FC's conflicting objectives

The main aim of the FC is quite clear, and was stated by a former chairman: 'We must not forget that the long-term aim of the Commission is to plant and manage trees for timber production and at the same time help and encourage private forestry to do the same' (*F&BT* May 1978). But pressure from environmental interests led to an obligation being imposed, under the Countryside Acts of 1967 and 1968, for the FC to 'have regard to the desirability of conserving the natural beauty and amenity of the countryside'. During the 1985 debates on the Wildlife and Countryside (Amendment) Bill, attempts were made to impose a duty on the FC of the furtherance of conservation. But this was opposed by the ministers concerned, doubtless because of pressure from the forestry lobby, and the FC is now obliged only 'to endeavour to achieve a reasonable balance' between the interests of forestry and those of the environment.

These obligations, and the curious dual role of the FC create a maze of contradictory objectives (Table 9.1), which conflict with the mutual goal of state and private forestry to expand afforestation. As the NAO (1986) has noted: 'Each of the secondary objectives to some extent conflicts with the primary objective of efficient wood supply; conversely the priority given to wood supplies limits the extent to which other objectives can be achieved.' The vague and unconvincing remit of trying to achieve 'a reasonable balance' is now left to fester at the centre of the conflicting objectives of the FC, leading to the acrimonious controversies that are routine in the upland countryside. The key conservation problem over blanket afforestation remains as stated by the NCC (1986): 'Pursuit of an open-ended, geographically undefined strategy

Table 9.1: *The Forestry Commission's contradictory objectives*

As Forestry Authority:		Possible conflicts with:
A1	to develop and ensure the best use of forest resources	A3 E3 E5 E6
A2	to promote the development of the wood using industry and its efficiency	A3 E3 E6
A3	to endeavour to achieve a reasonable balance between the interests of forestry and those of the environment	A1 A2 E1 E2 E3 E5
A4	to encourage good forestry practice in private woodlands through advice and schemes of financial assistance and by controls on felling	A2
A5	to advance knowledge and understanding of forestry and trees in the countryside	
A6	to undertake research relevant to the needs of forestry	
A7	to combat forest and tree pests and diseases	
A8	to advise and assist with safety and training in forestry	

As Forestry Enterprise:		
E1	To develop its forests for the production of wood for industry by extending and improving the forest estate	A3 E3 E4 E6
E2	to manage its estate economically and efficiently, and to account for its activities to ministers and parliament	A3 A4 E3 E4 E5 E6
E3	to protect and enhance the environment	A1 A2 A3 E1 E2 E5
E4	to provide recreational facilities	E1 E2
E5	to stimulate and support employment and the local economy in rural areas by the development of forests, including the establishment of new plantations, and of the wood-using industry	A3 E2 E3 E6
E6	to foster a harmonious relationship between forestry and other land-use interests, including agriculture	E1 E2 E5

Source: Forestry Commission objectives taken from *Forest Facts 2* (FC 1987c)

of expansion is incompatible with any realistic interpretation of balance.'

Forestry clearance and the RACs

The battleground where the reasonable balance is fought out is the system of voluntary consultation administered by the FC, which has to be endured before FC planting grants are paid. The consultation process has gradually evolved since 1974 in the face of outside pressures, and depends on the scale and location of the planting proposals, and often on local agreements between the FC and other agencies involved.

Afforestation proposals over 50 acres (20 ha) on land used for rough grazing in England and Wales, are referred to the Ministry of Agriculture, Fisheries and Food. In Scotland proposals to afforest more than 100 acres (40 ha) of hill land are referred to the Department of Agriculture and Fisheries for Scotland (DAFS). The local planning authority is consulted about the landscape and amenity aspects. This might involve a regional authority (in Scotland), county council, district council or a national park authority. If a planting scheme is part of an SSSI the NCC is consulted. The Countryside Commission is consulted on schemes in National Parks or AONBs, and the CCS is consulted over schemes in Scotland's National Scenic Areas.

If agreement cannot be reached at this first stage of consultation, the scheme is referred to the appropriate RAC, which can take six months or more to arrange. These Committees have no power to approve or reject the scheme, but merely seek to try to reach a compromise. If this is not possible the Forestry Commissioners are consulted. They have the power to reject a scheme but cannot approve it without the consent of the appropriate minister, or Secretary of State, who usually makes a visit to the site or sends a representative, which normally takes another six months or a year.

There are a number of flaws in the consultation process which have led to its being discredited. Firstly, there is the problem that the FC itself controls the process, and the local FC forest district manager is usually responsible for the consultations. He or she is forced into the uncomfortable position of having to juggle the ungainly list of the FC's conflicting objectives whilst removing his or her Forestry Enterprise 'hat' and substituting one labelled Forestry Authority. This is not an easy task, for the Enterprise 'hat' will have been worn with conviction and enthusiasm all through a career involving an academic training by other foresters, and immersion in an organisation which is devoted to the expansion of afforestation. It simply does not work. In five years as an acquisition manager I was in no doubt whose side the FC was on.

It is also contentious that half of the RAC which considers a forestry scheme consists of persons with overt forestry interests, often including commercial foresters, forestry lobbyists and investors. Their considerations are disgracefully confidential, and their report to the FC is secret.

Finally, the remit of the RAC to seek a compromise is frequently unhelpful. The conservationists' case might well be opposition to afforestation on any part of the site, in an attempt to balance the spread of blanket afforestation in the district as a whole. For them, a compromise involving partial afforestation is clearly a defeat. For the forestry lobbyists, however, a compromise is commercially acceptable, for half a planting contract is better than none. Having commenced planting on the site they can reapply for further clearance in five years' time, with every prospect of success. Compromise is a means by which the forestry lobby gets almost what it wants, whilst being able to claim that it has gone some way to meeting environmental concerns.

The evolution of the consultation system

In the golden days of afforestation, before the closure of the Basis II Dedication Scheme in 1972, planting grants were paid almost automatically, as long as the land was technically plantable. Further consultation was only needed if the land was in a National Park:

'I well remember the days when land acquisition depended only upon the availability of money. If you had a "client", then you bought. Having done a deal, you then wrote to the Forestry Commission stating your intention to enter into a Basis II Scheme which, subject only to technical approval, was normally granted at once. The fencers, the ploughmen and the planters moved in on the next day' (*F&BT* February 1985).

Foresters saw the development of the consultation system, through the Basis III Dedication Scheme and the FGS, as a considerable loss of power: 'The really sad feature of the sorry Basis III episode is the way in which the Forestry Commission has given away power, apparently in favour of influence' (*F&BT* March/April 1977).

Staff at the head of the FC realised that they were fighting a wider battle as the FC chairman implied when he defended the Basis III Scheme at the TGO annual general meeting in 1977: 'With all its difficulties and delays . . . it is the best we can do in this day and age'. He was aware of the private sector's opposition to the scheme which was seen as cumbersome, time-wasting and expensive, but he realised that the scheme was a bulwark against 'the much greater risk of the extension of planning control by local authorities to all forestry operations . . . We may appear to have lost a battle but there has been a useful regrouping of the forces involved and we are in much better shape for the rest of the campaign' (*F&BT* March/April 1977).

When J. Dickson retired as director general of the FC, it was reported that 'he did a great deal in preventing forestry from coming under planning control in the face of "vociferous opposition from environmental bodies" ' (*F&BT* March/April 1977).

Elements of the forestry lobby are now beginning to think that the consultation process has become so complex that the preparation of a detailed strategy for the future of afforestation in some parts of Britain would be a lesser evil. But a Secretary at the Scottish Department of Agriculture sounded a warning that such a strategy would lead to increased statutory control:

'The Government, I assure you, has no wish to hasten down that path. But it would be, or would be seen by many to be, a logical consequence of comprehensive planning. I sometimes wonder if those who criticise us from within the industry for a lack of planning are always aware of that logic' (*Scotsman* 1987).

As part of its long battle to maintain control over the consultation process, the forestry lobby made further concessions in 1987. All cases referred to the RACs will now have to be advertised publicly so that interested parties can comment (*F&BT* February 1988). The forestry lobby is quite content to go on tinkering with the RAC system, which remains secretive and partial, and studiously avoids major reform.

Commercial pressures

The delays caused by the consultation process are a considerable source of irritation to the afforestation companies and their clients, formerly anxious to plant trees before the end of the tax year. 'For Schedule D planters, speed of acquisition is often most important . . . The three months mentioned in the Basis III leaflet is a very long time to remain uncertain about the viability of a forestry development. The purchaser may have got fed up and gone elsewhere, or the vendor had a change of heart' (*F&BT* January/February 1977).

Tilhill Forestry lamented the fact that 'every private practitioner involved in land acquisition for planting has experienced all kinds of delays, and frustration in dealing with the non-statutory process of Basis III consultation' (*F&BT* April 1981). EFG thought: 'The consultative process has become lengthy and involved, creating a major constraint on land availability at the end of the fiscal year' (EFG 1987).

The ambiguous, dual role of the FC, as controller and promoter of afforestation, has helped to create a very unsatisfactory state of affairs. A spokesman (Survival Anglia 1988) stated that if the FC had known in 1977, what it now knows of the biological importance of the Flow Country, then things would have been very different. But in that case, why did the FC continue to go on giving private foresters the go-ahead to continue planting there?:

'Well, the problem is that we have started. People have made an investment and there's a lot of people working here. There's a lot of equipment committed. And whilst we would expect the rate of planting in the Flow Country to go down, and there's very little chance of it staying at the level it has been in the last few years, to stop suddenly would be very, very disruptive.'

Defending the RACs

The RACs, with their contingent of forestry interests, are of crucial importance in maintaining the power of the forestry lobby and avoiding planning control. Spokesmen go to great lengths to demonstrate how well they think the existing arrangements work. The TGUK was well aware of the importance of the RACs: 'We should retain these at all costs' (F&BT August 1984).

The Secretary of State for Scotland spoke about the consultation process as reported at a TGO annual general meeting:

'On frustrations felt by woodland owners about consultation procedures, Mr Younger said that they were vital in order to resist pressures which sought to control forestry developments . . . "we must be able to demonstrate that the existing consultation procedures do work and that decisions reached on planting and felling proposals are fair and sensible" ' (F&BT March 1983).

By contrast the RSPB's views on the RACs were summed up in a letter to the FC: 'To be frank we consider the RACs to be partial, over secretive, and offering nothing more than a cosmetic gloss to the FC's activities.'

A frequent tactic used by forestry interests, in an attempt to demonstrate the fairness of the RAC system, is to quote statistics. The starting point is often to add the number of felling licence applications to the total of all planting proposals, whether the latter are 0.6 acres (0.25 ha) or 4,000 acres (1,600 ha) in size, so that the largest possible number is created. For example, the FC chairman wrote that 26,000 felling and planting applications were made between 1974 and 1985, and that only 68 could not be agreed at the first stage of the consultation process and had to go on to be considered by an RAC (*Scotsman* 12 September 1985). Of these, 40 went on to be examined by ministers. What such figures may disguise is the highly contentious nature of many large afforestation schemes, hidden by the number of routine licences for felling and thinning, and the large number of straightforward, small planting schemes. It must be remembered that blanket afforestation in Britain is carried on by just 40 to 60 large schemes every year.

It is interesting to follow the publicity given to Devall and Brotherton's research on afforestation consultations in the National Parks (1986). The results have been avidly seized upon by the forestry lobby (*F&BT* November 1987): 'They provide no basis for the conservationists' calls to extend planning controls in National Parks.'

The research of Devall and Brotherton involved an examination of 250 afforestation proposals over the ten years from 1974 to 84, in the National Parks of England and Wales. The key to interpreting the findings is that almost two-thirds of the proposals were for areas of less than about 60 acres (25 ha), and three quarters were for areas less than about 125 acres (50 ha). These are small forestry schemes indeed, and very different to the blanket planting schemes that are causing such problems in Scotland. It is not surprising that the great majority of the small schemes were acceptable with only minor changes. There were only 34 afforestation proposals, or an average of little more than three for each National Park over the ten years, which exceeded 250 acres (100 ha) in size. These larger schemes, however, accounted for over 60 per cent of the total area of proposed planting. They also aroused most concern from the national park authorities and 21 of them were drastically reduced in size, withdrawn or rejected, after consultation.

The importance of large-scale afforestation schemes in extending the total area of blanket afforestation in the highland region of Scotland can be seen from Hetherington's (1988) analysis of planting schemes between 1981 and 1985. He found that a 56 per cent majority of afforestation schemes were less than 124 acres (50 ha) in size, but these only occupied a tiny 3 per cent of the total proposed planting area. The remainder of the planting schemes, each over 124 acres in size, covered a total of 139,432 acres (56,427 ha) or 97 per cent of the total area. Just 18 large schemes over the five year period, each over 2,000 acres (800 ha) in size, covered 69,396 acres (28,084 ha) or nearly half the total of proposed afforestation.

The growing tide of opposition

So great is the tide of opposition to blanket afforestation in England and Wales that almost any large planting scheme is now strongly opposed. Referral to the RAC is almost inevitable, predictably followed by a failure to reach a compromise, and a subsequent ministerial visit.

Until recently there has been less opposition to forestry in Scotland. Dr Jean Balfour, former CCS chairman was able to comment that: 'Scotland did not suffer from the "anti-forestry" attitude found in the South. It was, she said, treated in a positive way in regional policy plans with planning authorities treating planting proposals in a "relaxed way" ' (*F&BT* November 1979).

This lack of opposition was partly due to the much larger area of hill land available, and the less populated countryside. But now that blanket afforestation has almost saturated some areas with conifers, and as concern has mounted about the destruction of the Flow Country, opposition to forestry in Scotland has steadily increased (see Table 9.2).

Table 9.2: *The growing tide of opposition to afforestation – controversial schemes which attracted media coverage during 1986/87*

The Flow Country	– widespread objections to afforestation of tens of thousands of acres of land, led by the RSPB and the NCC.
Gleann Dubh, Perthshire	– protests from eight groups and public bodies including CCS and SWT over tree planting on thousands of acres of land near Balquhidder.
Ashstead Fell, Cumbria	– vigorous opposition to a 400 acre (160 ha) conifer plantation, on the fringe of the Lake District, proposed by EFG.
Dent Fell, Cumbria	– opposition to a 500 acre (200 ha) scheme proposed by EFG on the western edge of the Lake District.
Leap Hill, Ashkirk	– hill land in the Borders purchased at forestry prices by a local landowner in order to prevent afforestation by EFG.
Raydale House, Yorkshire Dales	– planting proposed on 300 acres (120 ha) in the National Park.
North York Moors	– proposals to afforest 309 acres (125 ha) in the National Park.

Table 9.2 – cont.

Priest Hill, Newcastleton	– the entire local community opposed 420 acres (170 ha) of planting overlooking the town, in an area already blanketed with conifers.
Isle of Bute	– 2,000 acres (810 ha) of land bought for afforestation by a Canadian timber company. Tilhill to carry out the planting in an NSA.
Glen Lednock, Perthshire	– 1,000 people sign a petition opposing the afforestation of 750 acres (300 ha).
Glen Lochay, Perthshire	– opposition to planting of 1,750 acres (710 ha) from the Regional Council, NCC, and the Scottish Wild Land Group.
Moness, Perthshire	– proposed afforestation of 600 acres (240 ha) of land adjoining a beauty spot near Aberfeldy.
Criffel, Dumfries	– a 675 acre (270 ha) planting scheme on a spectacular landmark in a Scottish NSA. Petition signed by 1,500 local people, objectors include WWF, RSPB, SWT, Association for the Protection of Rural Scotland.
Milton of Clova, Angus	– strong reservations from CCS on 777 acres (310 ha) of proposed planting adjoining an NSA.
Howpasley, Eskdalemuir	– 1,440 acres (580 ha) of land under threat of afforestation, despite the receipt of large agricultural grants in the past.
Moulin Moor, Perthshire	– archaeological remains threatened by a large afforestation scheme.
Overkirkhope, Ettrick	– EFG propose a 900 acre (360 ha) scheme despite a unanimous local vote of opposition.
Gorrenberry, Newcastleton	– high-quality sheep farm of 1,200 acres (490 ha) threatened by afforestation. 600 local people petition.
Drumelzier, Tweeddale	– 286 acre (115 ha) scheme opposed by Ramblers Association, NCC, CCS, RSPB and local people.
Blaen Nedd Isaf, Brecon Beacons	– proposal to plant 72 acres (30 ha) of the National Park approved by Secretary of State for Wales.
Craig y Garn, Wales	– Flintshire Woodlands application to afforest goes to a ministerial decision.
Dyfed, Wales	– controversial afforestation schemes of 240 acres (100 ha) at Barn Ceirch and 300 acres (120 ha) at Bwlch-y-garreg.

Concessions to the environment

A long battle has been fought over the location and extent of afforestation. A similar battle has been waged over the design of plantations. Management of small woodlands, landscaping, planting broadleaves and consideration of wildlife impact, are all too often seen by foresters as concessions which have to be made to environmentalists, in order to protect wider forestry interests. Moncrieff (1985) summed up the responsibilities of foresters and their clients: 'if they do not take advantage of the opportunity to improve their landscaping, their wildlife and general ecological management and their public relations, they will face the risk that eventually new conifer planting in the uplands will be brought to a halt by a coalition of environmental interests.'

Such attitudes, however, fail to confront the key conservation problem. No amount of landscaping can compensate for the loss of open habitat and semi-natural vegetation with its characteristic wildlife. It is merely the formula to be allowed to continue blanket afforestation. A similar misapprehension pervades foresters' attitudes to planting broadleaved trees. They think that if enough are planted, generally in narrow ribbons along streams and around the boundaries of conifer plantations, then conservation problems will be overcome: 'Foresters are blamed for damaging the flora and fauna of moorland sites. To meet such criticism, foresters adopt codes of practice to ensure that wildlife damage is minimised . . . the most important additional feature is the species diversity, and in particular the use of native broadleaves' (Ogilvy 1986).

The FC itself is also attempting to maximise the public relations value of planting broadleaves and now has a guideline that all upland plantations should contain a token 5 per cent (FC 1988). Is this what the Forestry Authority has decided is a reasonable balance? Once again, the key environmental issue, that some areas of the uplands simply should not be afforested, is totally and deliberately avoided.

Planting without grants

There is obviously a strictly finite amount of plantable hill land in Britain, which is gradually being used up by the afforestation companies that depend upon new planting for their profits. Although there was no reason why the amount of land cleared for forestry should ever have matched the number of investors seeking tax avoidance in any year, the afforestation industry sought to create the myth of a land shortage, despite the secret land banks of

Figure 9.1 *Nothing is sacred – the scars of forestry ploughing ruin a unique beauty spot at St Mary's Loch, near Moffat, south Scotland*

Figure 9.2 *Cosmetic fringes of broadleaves are increasingly used to hide blanket conifer afforestation. Here the broadleaves are planted in polythene tree shelters. Near Carsphairn, south Scotland*

unplanted forestry land. The forestry lobby then used the mythical shortage to campaign for yet more land to be cleared for planting. The TGUK described the situation as 'the pressure cooker' that had developed through the shortage of available planting land (*Scotsman* 25 March 1986).

The supply of planting land that can be afforested with FC grant aid depends on clearance through a consultation system that is only voluntary. Foresters, as we have seen, regard this as a time-consuming, bureaucratic frustration. During the heyday of tax avoidance, forestry clearance of land only led to an inflation of its price, so there was an obvious temptation for an investor to ignore the consultation process, buy the land cheaply, and plant it without grants. This was made possible for private investors because of another shameful loophole – full tax avoidance was obtainable even if they ignored the consultation process. Obviously, if the consultation process had been abandoned on a large scale, there would have been calls for planning control and the FC would have lost its role as Forestry Authority. The FC's fear of this led to the Kinnell scandal which broke in 1985.

The Kinnell scandal

Capt. Baillie-Hamilton purchased 3,000 acres (1,200 ha) of the Kinnell estate and then employed Tilhill Forestry to start ploughing up part of the land, making it clear he was going to plant it, even though there was no forestry clearance.

The FC was highly embarrassed, but completely powerless to prevent this blatant violation of the 'gentleman's agreement' that planting would not take place without clearance. In an attempt to solve the problem the FC asked Baillie-Hamilton to stop work and to re-apply for clearance (*Scotsman* 4 December 1985). He was given retrospective approval and the planting grant that went with it. The decision went against the normal rule that five years must elapse before a re-application can be made on the same land, and that clearance cannot be given after work has started on a forestry scheme. The excuse given was that the estate was no longer a viable agricultural unit because it had been split into lots.

The Ombudsman was called in but rejected charges of maladministration, and his report disclosed the fears of the Secretary of State for Scotland, and the FC chairman, that if planting went ahead there would be criticism of the voluntary consultation process:

'Sir David said any breach would lead to strong pressure from the environmental lobby for statutory control. "The Secretary of State saw the main difficulty being the likelihood that even if the application was refused, Captain Baillie-Hamilton would go ahead without grant aid. He said that on other grounds he would be happy to turn the application down, but that he was reluctant to take a decision which would inevitably lead to criticism of the system for dealing with planting applications" ' (*Scotsman* 27 April 1987).

Crichness and Shielsknowe

Before details of the Kinnell scandal emerged, there were two further, major breaches of the voluntary consultation system, where large areas of land were planted without grants. Crichness was a 2,000 acre (800 ha) hill farm on the open moors of the Lammermuir Hills in south-east Scotland. The vendor had tried to obtain forestry clearance to raise the price of some of the land, but only had approval for a series of shelterbelts (see Chapter 10). This integrated scheme was of no interest to the afforestation industry. Instead the whole farm was purchased by forestry investors advised by David Goss and Associates. They planted a 500 acre block (200 ha) without grants in the spring of 1985. Further blocks of land on the farm have now been planted, presumably with grant aid, since the viability of the farm had been ruined.

The second violation occurred at Shielsknowe, where Tilhill planted 500 acres (200 ha) without grants on the hills near Carter Bar. Northumberland National Park lies just over the border to the south, and there would have been a much greater public outcry if the same thing had happened there. Thankfully, the closure of the tax-avoidance loophole should make planting without grants a thing of the past.

Dissent in the forestry lobby

The forestry world was deeply concerned that planting without grants would jeopardise the consultation process and lead to calls for planning control. EFG (1985b) voiced these fears:

'The alternative of bringing forestry under formal planning control is not one which could in any respect be claimed to be in the best interests of either forestry or the country. There have been signs recently that those whose interests and sense of responsibility do not extend beyond the opportunity of short-term gain are prepared to ignore the consultation processes and to plant regardless. That is most regrettable.'

Tanarus spoke out eloquently: 'There can rarely have been such a short-sighted, wrong-headed decision in the history of private forestry . . .' (*F&BT* January 1986).

The attack on DAFS

In the wake of planting without grants conservationists may have felt that their arguments for improved controls over afforestation had been strengthened, but P. Moore (1985) sounded a warning:

'The companies are going to say that planting without grants and the problems at Creag Meagaidh are caused because insufficient planting land is being made available. The Department of Agriculture in Scotland is being singled out for particular attack and pressure. It seems that 60 square miles of afforestation every year are not enough for the companies, and it is clear their demands will always be insatiable.'

The speaker at the EFG's annual luncheon stressed the need for more afforestation and questioned the need for a 'veto' by agricultural departments for farmers wishing to transfer land from food to trees (*F&BT* May 1985). Another spokesman kept up the pressure at a seminar held on one of the Duke of Buccleuch's estates: Today's battles, he said, were not – as in the past – with farmers but in Scotland with the Department of Agriculture and Fisheries. 'This body often blindly objects to afforestation schemes taking a (some would say brave but in my view, foolhardy) stance on thin ice' (*F&BT* December 1985).

Further challenges to DAFS followed: 'Technical land shortages created by difficulties in forestry grant scheme approval by the Department of Agriculture (in Scotland) only serve to distort the price of land . . . farmers and landowners should be free to plant trees without the threat of grants being withdrawn' (*F&BT* February 1986).

The impression given from this level of campaigning is that DAFS took a negative view of afforestation and opposed almost every afforestation scheme. Yet this view is clearly unsustainable in view of the annual afforestation programme at the time, and the amount of forestry cleared land in the secret land banks. As a DAFS spokesman pointed out: 'We have habitually cleared between 70–80 per cent of all FGS applications without demur and a further 10 per cent with agreed modifications after discussion. Our record in relation to forestry could not remotely be described as hostile' (*F&BT* May 1986).

What DAFS had been concerned to do was to allow the viability of individual hill farms to be maintained, by ensuring that too much land was not sold off for afforestation. It also sought to restrict the amount of scarce, better-quality grazing that was planted on such farms. But, helped by the increasingly fashionable preoccupation with reducing agricultural surpluses the forestry lobby went on to overcome any residual opposition from DAFS. The 'surpluses' argument was particularly irrelevant, as afforestation of poor-quality land in the hills does nothing to reduce beef, dairy and grain mountains produced by intensive, chemical-based farming in the lowlands.

In the spring of 1986 the Secretary of State for Scotland 'delighted timber growers by announcing that a wider range of land would be permitted for afforestation in Scotland' (*F&BT* May 1986). No consultation at all is now needed with DAFS on planting schemes involving less than 100 acres (40 ha) of hill land, and there is a general presumption in favour of afforestation on such land.

The forestry lobby subsequently made grateful noises about being able to reach the annual target of the time of 74,000 acres (30,000 ha) of afforestation. During 1985/86 DAFS went on to release 112,430 acres (45,500 ha) of hill land for afforestation, amounting to some 175 sq miles. This was a larger area than the Isle of Wight and twice the area planted or released in Scotland the year before.

SSSIs under threat

An application to afforest an SSSI is subject to the normal process of voluntary consultation, although the NCC is formally consulted in addition. If agreement cannot be reached the case is referred to the RAC, and then to the appropriate minister, so that ultimately the prevention of afforestation on an SSSI depends on the political whim of the government of the day.

The Wildlife and Countryside Act of 1981 created controversial and far reaching implications for SSSIs, by establishing the principle of compensation. The owners of such sites became entitled to financial compensation if they were prevented from carrying out damaging operations, even if such operations would not have been profitable without public subsidies in the first place. The Act seemed to give legal recognition to the concept of an automatic right to grants from the public purse. The market value of land designated as an SSSI has clearly been increased by the compensation principle.

The saga of the attempted afforestation of Creag Meagaidh, a Scottish hill massif rising to 3,700 ft (1,130 m) above Loch Laggan, and an SSSI, is instructive. Fountain Forestry purchased about **10,000 acres (4,000 ha) of land at Creag Meagaidh for just**

£300,000 or £30 per acre (£75 per ha). The company then applied
for forestry clearance on 2,700 acres (1,100 ha) of the lower slopes,
standing to gain planting land worth £800,000. It is unusual for
an afforestation company to speculate by buying land without
clearance in this way, but if the application was rejected compensation was payable, so that Fountain Forestry could hardly lose.
Despite objections from the NCC, the FC fully supported the
scheme, as did the RAC. The Secretary of State for Scotland proposed the compromise that 1,300 acres (525 ha) should be planted.
Eventually the NCC bought the site as a nature reserve for £430,000,
because the Secretary of State's decision had inflated the land price.

There must be fears that the level of financial compensation
involved under the Act will inhibit objections to damaging developments on SSSIs in future:

'In two instances, the NCC paid in total over £0.5 million to
prevent afforestation on less than 5,000 acres (2,000 ha). With the
government's expressed desire to increase our home grown timber
base, it is hard to imagine continuing expenditure at this level to
maintain land in its unproductive state' (Ogilvy 1986).

The drive for more land

Attempts by environmentalists to restrict the spread of afforestation can be likened to a temporary dam holding back the pent-up
demands of the afforestation companies for the planting land on
which to generate their profits. But, no matter where the dam is
built, a new surge of afforestation breaks through somewhere else.
As Moncrieff (1986) wrote: 'New planting continued in the far
north and even increased – but there are now signs that it is in
decline and if more land becomes available in more accessible
locations then it may cease altogether.'

The threat to common land

The existence of large areas of unenclosed common land in the hills
of England and Wales has been crucial in protecting them from
the blanket afforestation seen in Scotland, where most hill land
is privately owned without common rights. Great tracts of the
Pennines, and substantial areas of National Parks such as the
Yorkshire Dales and Lake District, are protected in this way.
Common rights such as grazing or peat cutting can prevent a
landowner from selling the freehold for afforestation.

It should come as no surprise that the forestry lobby has
campaigned vigorously for a change in the legislation to allow

afforestation of common land. Reacting to the FC's *The Wood Production Outlook: a Review* (1977) (see below), EFG pointed out the difficulties of obtaining suitable planting land:
'There are substantial areas of land currently being used for hill farming, sporting purposes or common or crofting land which are technically suitable for afforestation but which are, because of title or ownership uncertainties, not coming forward onto the market: they represent a major source of potential forestry land' (*F&BT* November/December 1978).

The FC chairman said that 'while farming land would be involved, the first areas to be planted up should be grouse moors, deer forests and common land . . .' (*F&BT* July 1980). EFG's chairman is reported to have highlighted 'the job creating potential of afforest-ing the hundreds of thousands of hectares of Britain's wasted, unproductive and unmanaged woodlands and common land . . .' (*F&BT* April 1982). The theme was taken up by the Secretary of State for Wales who 'promised to seek solutions for making better use of the vast areas of common land, particularly in Wales, to develop opportunities for increased forest planting' (*F&BT* April 1982).

The propaganda war

Unfortunately, environmentalists failed to capitalise on the 1972 Treasury Review and the forestry lobby redoubled its efforts. By 1977 the FC had produced *The Wood Production Outlook: a Review*. This was written by five senior FC officers, a member of the Department of Industry, and a representative from the Building Research Establishment. Three possible planting programmes were put forward: no new planting, planting at the current rate, or a substantial acceleration to 74,000 acres (30,000 ha) per year. The latter was considered a 'prudent investment', but it was not until 1986 that the lobby managed to establish this open-ended pro-gramme as official 'government' policy.

Although several private sector groups thought that the forestry case was understated, the forestry lobby celebrated *The Wood Production Outlook: a Review*, produced by its sympathisers, and gave it excellent reviews (*F&BT* November/December 1978):

'An excellent document . . .' *Royal Forestry Society*
' "A useful preliminary" to the development of a forestry pro-gramme based on the planting of a further 1.8m ha by 2025.' *Institute of Foresters*
'Tended to understate the case for forestry . . .' *TGUK*

'An excellent piece of work . . .' *Tilhill*

Not content with this, the forestry lobby went on to produce the CAS report, *Strategy for the UK Forest Industry*, in 1980. This elaborate study began where the FC left off, and advocated annual planting programmes of 74,000–148,000 acres (30,000–60,000 ha), with detailed tables showing how much afforestation would have to be accepted in National Parks.

The forestry lobby was naturally pleased at the predictable outcome of the CAS report and thought that it would 'provide valuable ammunition in the battle to persuade Government and Treasury of the need to boost dramatically future supplies of British-grown timber' (*F&BT* July 1979). Further laudatory reviews were guaranteed by the incestuous nature of the forestry lobby:

'Should form the basis of national forest policy . . .' *SWOA*
'Long term confidence is the essential incentive . . .' *TGO*
'Described by many as the best of its kind ever put together . . .'
F&BT April 1980

But during the 1980s the afforestation industry's public relations image aroused great concern in the forestry lobby. The lobby's response was the glossy booklet, *The Forestry and Woodland Code* (1985), published by TGUK. This 'is about forestry practice in harmony with nature and the community' and acknowledges that 'countryside is an important element in the quality of life', pointing out that woodlands must be managed with an understanding of this 'as far as possible . . . if forestry is to continue to enjoy public support'. Much space in the Code is taken up by twelve pictures of flowers and animals. There are nine general views, mostly taken across scenic water features, and eight pictures of broadleaved woodland. There are only six pictures of upland conifer afforestation, carefully enhanced by open roads and rides, and several of the pictures seem to have been taken through a softening filter or else are slightly out of focus. In terms of management guidelines the Code says little, and could be summarised as: don't plant too close to streams, roads or rocky outcrops; do plant a few broadleaves; and keep the grey squirrels under control.

Despite the best efforts of the TGUK, criticisms of upland afforestation grew apace during the mid-1980s. An essential document was the NCC's *Nature Conservation and Afforestation in Britain* (1986). This remained a very strong condemnation of upland afforestation practices despite attempts by forestry lobbyists to use their influence to dilute its criticisms. The TGUK attempted to pre-empt the NCC report by publishing its own *Afforestation and*

Nature Conservation: Interactions (1986). Once again the forestry lobby relied on academics from university forestry departments for the bulk of their competing report. The TGUK's own slant was clear in the preface:

'As a nation, we must decide how much of our land resource we (and our successors in the next century) will wish or can afford to "preserve" as wilderness, where wildlife conservation is preferred to development, job creation and in terms of fragile rural communities, human conservation also.'

A thinly veiled challenge to the NCC and its legitimate role followed: 'Problems also arise when agencies whose responsibility is to gather and present facts on important issues, may claim to interpret the decisions which, in their view, ought to follow. More constructively, their primary function through powers of designation where appropriate, is to draw attention to features of special importance and by identifying the ecological facts, provide the information to those whose task it is to decide on matters of optimum land-use when weighing up the balance.'

The most serious threat to the forestry lobby since the 1972 Treasury Review, arose from the NAO study of the FC in 1986. Once again, an independent, economic scrutiny of afforestation produced serious criticisms. Although the report said little about private afforestation, the forestry lobby responded by setting up the FICGB and produced *The Forestry Industry Response* within the month (Firn, Crichton and Roberts 1987). The FICGB's response was at least noteworthy for the nostalgic attempt to resurrect the strategic defence justification for afforestation, for the timber might be needed as a future 'war's aftermath would be long and bitter'.

The FC's role in the propaganda war is extremely revealing. Its latest foray is the glossy magazine *Forest Life*, the second issue (1988) of which is chiefly remarkable for outstanding flower photography. The Sitka spruce is shamefully neglected pictorially, although one tree is shown being subjected to the humiliation of felling to protect a stone circle. Presumably the FC can justify this expenditure on public relations magazines under its Forestry Authority objectives of 'advancing knowledge and understanding of forestry' or 'promoting the development of the wood-using industry'. It does seem a distinct advantage to the forestry lobby to have a government department as one of its arms, and one which many environmental pressure groups must envy. The FC seems free to promote the views of the forestry lobby, most assertively, and at the taxpayers' expense.

Fear of the media

A striking feature of the effects of sustained criticism on the forestry lobby is its fear of the media. If an unflattering report is carried in the press or on television, the lobby's instinctive reaction is to blame inherent media hostility. This seems to be a clear symptom of the 'group-think' described in Chapter 8. A BBC 2 'Newsnight' programme came in for a sharp attack: 'That a powerful, public information medium should be abused and used as a propaganda weapon was a disgrace' (*F&BT* April 1984).

By the spring of 1988 the forestry lobby had realised that its public image was suffering badly, largely because of the excesses of Flow Country afforestation. The media continued to receive the blame, for there was no question that the forestry lobby itself might be wrong: 'Media and political attacks on private afforestation practices rose to danger level, predictably in the lead up to next week's Budget. "Everybody" clambered aboard . . . for a safe position from which to denounce the beleaguered industry and all its ways' (*F&BT* March 1988).

A Survival Anglia television programme on the Flow Country, 'Paradise Ploughed', brought forth great scorn. But at least the forestry lobby has displayed an even-handed antipathy to both public and private sector broadcasting: 'Towards this northern fastness Dr David Bellamy hied himself to present one of his inimitable, partisan televisual forays among the environmentalists, with token appearances by the humble forester. Emotion ran boringly high but facts and historical context were low script priorities' (*F&BT* March 1988).

The final blow came when the Chancellor of the Exchequer abolished tax-avoidance incentives for afforestation in the 1988 Budget. His decision was instantly blamed on media hostility: 'Press hyperbole has dogged our industry and Nigel Lawson's decision is likely to remembered as one of the worst examples. The financial support, numbers employed and votes at risk in the forestry industry are tiny' (*F&BT* April 1988).

The forestry lobby seems firmly entrenched in the view that it is its public relations effort that needs to be improved and not policies. In 1988 a three-day course was offered at the School of Agricultural and Forest Sciences at Bangor University. Delegates were lured to the course, costing them £400 each, as follows:

'In the early years of the twentieth century Gifford Pinchot the first Chief Forester of the United States Forest Service wrote concerning forestry practice that "something like 90 per cent is propaganda." Eighty years later most British foresters are realising the truth of this statement but are not equipped to present their case with the panache and professionalism of many organisations and individuals.'

After the 'Big Bang'

The forestry lobby is preparing for a major propaganda campaign to recover from the setback it received from the closure of the tax loophole in the 1988 Budget. Its key priority is to ensure that afforestation contracts in the uplands can continue. An immediate reaction was that the new range of planting grants was not high enough to compensate for the loss of tax avoidance. An editorial in *F&BT* called for the large-scale, conifer planting grant to be raised to £400 per acre (£1,000 per ha) instead of the actual £250 per acre (£615 per ha), in an attempt to stem the likely fall in forestry land prices.

The main thrust of the campaign has centred on the target of 81,500 acres (33,000 ha) of upland planting. The chairman of EFG is concerned about future planting:

'The acid test will be whether the Government's planting targets are achieved. It may be that in the first year or two of the transitional period they will be. People already involved in a planting programme will continue for a while. After that, there must be considerable doubt. If the targets are not achieved, I hope that the Government will candidly recognise the flaws in their present measures and reconsider them – next time in consultation with those who have some experience of an important national activity' (Hansard 1988a).

Part Three

The Two Faces of British Forestry

═ 10 ═
Upland Forestry –
Second-rate Forests

The myth of integration

Integration between forestry and agriculture has always been a mysterious goal, never precisely defined, but paid effusive lip service by many farming and forestry lobbyists. In effect, integration was a notional, idealised balance between forestry and agriculture, where all of the hill land on a farm would not be simply blanketed with conifers. Instead, in this imaginary world, a carefully chosen area of land might be planted, or a series of shelter belts created, to the mutual benefit of farming and forestry.

Sadly, integration has never materialised under the incentives provided by tax avoidance or flat-rate planting grants. The afforestation of Crichness, described in Chapter 9, is a classic example. Instead of a series of shelterbelts which would have been approved by DAFS and local planners, blanket conifer planting was carried out which ignored the consultation process (Figure 10.1). This was the inevitable consequence of the commercial imperative to create a block of plantations that would be saleable to the secondary market in future years. Such blanket afforestation also minimises unit costs, and is a further result of flat-rate planting grants.

Planting ever-poorer land

To an extent, the afforestation of poor hill land is an inevitable consequence of a forestry policy that began by seeking to avoid a conflict with agriculture, a point made by the FC director-general:

'it has been a matter of policy to accord priority to food production and therefore it has only been land which falls outside that policy which has found its way into forestry. Of necessity it has been . . . right from the early days of the Commission, the poorest land and some of the most difficult climatic conditions that one finds in this country' (PAC 1987).

The problem of afforestation on poor land has grown steadily greater, however, as explained in Chapter 5. In the absence of proper controls, the drive for profitable planting contracts has pushed private afforestation onto ever poorer and higher land in

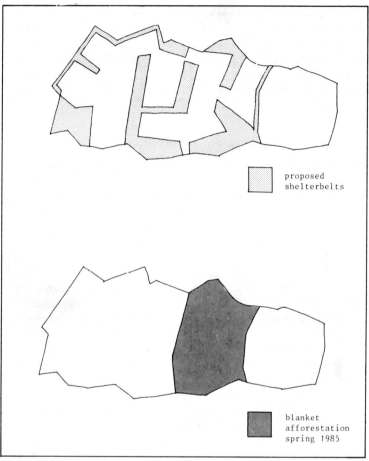

Figure 10.1 *The myth of integration – blanket afforestation at Crichness*
Source: Moore 1985

the most remote locations in Britain. The FC has also been guilty
of planting ever-poorer land. Finding itself a victim of the land price
spiral, it was unable to compete with the clients of afforestation
companies and could only afford to buy cheap land. This trend was
identified by the economic consultants, PIEDA, who reported that
the FC was planting more 'marginal' land, in general terms, than
it had been at the time of the 1972 Treasury Review (1986).
However, the FC is always able to retreat into its maze of conflicting objectives to excuse planting on remote and less fertile areas
as being carried out in order to maintain rural employment: 'It
does involve . . . returns which are quite low on sites which are
extremely infertile' (PAC 1987).

Technological progress in the development of afforestation techniques, fuelled by the insatiable demand for more planting land, has also led to poorer land being planted. An FC chief research officer noted that improved techniques 'led to productive planting on the poorest of upland peatlands and into severe exposure at up to 1,000 ft (300 m) in the north-western uplands and 2,000 ft (600 m) in more central and eastern areas' (*F&BT* October 1979).

Doubts about the Flow Country

Significantly, only one afforestation company has been active in the Flow Country. The other companies have been greatly concerned about this, not least because of the thousands of acres of planting contracts carried out without competition, amounting to about one-fifth of annual, upland afforestation at one stage (FC 1987e). At least one other company has made repeated visits to the flows, to see whether afforestation could be justified, but was put off by insect damage, likely wind problems, poor soils and transport difficulties. The other companies have also been concerned that the extremely bad publicity generated by the Flow Country planting would bring the whole of the afforestation industry into disrepute, but they have found it awkward to voice their criticisms without undermining the forestry industry. It is a measure of the strength of feeling within the forestry lobby that doubts about planting the poorest land, even made obliquely, have been made public at all.

An EFG (1985a) brochure shows a map of Scotland which excludes the Flow Country from the area of hill land shown as suitable for afforestation and states that: 'Land can be acquired at prices below £120 per acre but we consider that, although superficially attractive from a tax planning point of view, the investment will have a greater risk and a significantly lower rate of return.'

Moncrieff (1985) put the point about planting poor land more strongly: ' A more competitive market and the artificial shortage of planting land are dividing the industry between those who care more for the long-term and those who, at least to external appearances, will plant anything as long as it yields a short-term profit with scant regard for the environment, the long-term future of the industry or even, it seems, the ultimate interests of their clients' (1985).

Tilhill urged investors to 'keep in the quality end of the market and do not be swayed by the superficial attraction of "more acres for my money" ' (*F&BT* July 1984).

Catastrophic wind damage

Catastrophic windthrow (or windblow) is the term used by the FC itself for the damage caused by particularly severe gales. Little can be done to protect trees from such storms, and upland forests, high in the exposed hills, on poorly drained soils which inhibit root penetration, are especially vulnerable. Severe storms are supposed to have long recurrence periods, according to the FC (1985), and on average some part of the United Kingdom is affected about once every 15 years. Recent experience tends to suggest that catastrophic gales are affecting forests more frequently than this.

In January 1953, a gale blew down 1.5 million tonnes of timber in east Scotland, but the most notorious gale to affect conifer plantations so far was that of January 1968. The results were indeed catastrophic. The gale struck 13 per cent of Scotland's land area and caused immense damage to western and central forests. A total of 20,600 acres (8,300 ha) or 32 sq miles of plantation were blown over, involving 1.4 million tonnes of timber, some of which was still being cleared ten years later at Carron Valley Forest (Davies 1982). The FC had to pay subsidies amounting to £409,000 to get the timber transported to sawmills. Almost all of the damage occurred in areas with more than six hours of wind above 60 mph. A staggering 22 per cent of forests over 31 years of age in the damage zone were blown over, and there was a clear relationship between the height of the damaged trees, the elevation at which they were growing on the hills, and the amount of damage they sustained (FC 1971).

Further gales caused major windthrow in Scotland in January 1974. About 70,000 tonnes of timber were blown down, with south-west Scotland being the worst hit (*F&BT* February/March 1974). The next gale causing widespread forest damage was in January 1976, striking central Wales, the Midlands and East Anglia. About 612,000 tonnes of timber were blown over in FC forests, with considerable, but unquantified damage occurring in private forests as well (*F&BT* April/May 1976). If the same gale had struck the conifer plantations of Scotland, where a much greater proportion of the land is afforested, there would have been far greater damage still.

The most recent manifestation of catastrophic windthrow hit southern England in October 1987, and generated a great deal of publicity. It is estimated that 3.4 million tonnes of timber were blown down, and tragically, most of it was from broadleaved woodland (*F&BT* December 1987).

A truly frightening aspect of catastrophic windthrow is going to

Figure 10.2 *The tangled remains of windthrown Sitka spruce spoil the view alongside a 'scenic route' through the Forestry Commission's Galloway Forest Park in south Scotland*

Figure 10.3 *A hideous line of upturned root plates as Sitka spruce blows down near Straiton, Strathclyde Region, south Scotland*

be what happens when the next major gale strikes Scotland. Davies (1982) expressed his fears in an article entitled 'The Next Big One'. He pointed out that 14 years after the 1968 gale the total area of FC plantations in south Scotland that had reached the vulnerable age of 20 years had increased from 11,900 acres (4,800 ha) to about 83,000 acres (33,600 ha). He warned that these crops were mostly shallow-rooted spruces on wet, unstable soils, and acknowledged that the average height of the plantations above sea-level had slowly increased, obviously due to the fact that higher and higher land had been planted. He calculated there was seven times as much vulnerable FC plantation in south Scotland than at the time of the 1968 gale, and foresaw that 'by 1987 the overall area at risk will start to rise even faster as the huge forestry company plantings of the late 1960s are recruited'. The consequences of the next major gale to hit the conifer plantations on the hills of south Scotland are going to be truly appalling.

Endemic windthrow

Despite the spectacular damage of tangled, up-rooted trees and shattered stems, that is caused by catastrophic windthrow, the economic consequences of endemic windthrow are far more serious (FC 1985). Endemic windthrow arises as a result of normal winter gales with a relatively moderate mean speed of about 45 mph, gusting to 67 mph. Most forests in the uplands experience gales of this nature several times every year, and groups of vulnerable trees are often blown down throughout plantations at risk. At Eskdale-muir for example: 'Winds are often severe and gale force winds have been recorded in every month of the year' (EFG undated a).

Endemic windthrow determines the rotation lengths of upland conifer crops, and has a crucial effect on the rate of return on the investment. Trees which blow down prematurely, before timber of sufficient size for sawlogs is produced, yield a very low return. It is very revealing that in the early days of the FC in 1929, a statement by the Forestry Commissioners envisaged conifers coming to maturity in 60 to 100 years (*F&BT* December 1979). Even as late as 1977 the FC assumed a standard rotation of 55 years for most FC plantations. The sad fact is that many vulnerable crops are now blowing down at just 30–35 years of age, and sometimes at only 15–25 years old.

It is a tragedy for British forestry policy that over the last 30 years, about 20 per cent of the FC's timber production has had to be felled prematurely because of endemic windthrow, in addition to the 6 per cent that was damaged by catastrophic windthrow

(Rollinson 1985). The proportion of prematurely felled timber, representing a poor investment by the FC, is going to climb steadily as trees planted on increasingly poor land reach a vulnerable age.

Why afforestation continues on high risk land

Tanarus has identified 'the crux of the whole problem' of windthrow:

'We have been, and continue to be, obsessed with planting. Every inch must have a crop standing on it: if it's hill land and is bought for forestry, then planted it must be. And just as those pioneers who cleared the bush and forest found that some areas did not produce crops, so, I suspect, our successors will reclaim some of today's plantations where we have been a bit too precipitate with our blanket afforestation' (*F&BT* March 1979).

Despite the immense problems that wind damage has caused, and the untold crises in store, blanket afforestation of vulnerable land continues unabated. Much has to do with the structure of the afforestation industry, where crops are sold to the secondary market at ten or fifteen years of age when they are still too young to have been disturbed by gales. The pension funds, and other institutions that buy such plantations, effectively do so at a large discount, reflecting the tax avoidance or grant incentives received by the planters. This means that the institutions do not need to take account of the costs of establishment, which are effectively written off. Their valuation of a plantation is based solely on future expenditure and income. If the onset of windthrow is correctly predicted then they suffer no loss, but simply receive a return on their investment through timber income sooner rather than later. Massive subsidies to afforestation, without adequate scrutiny of the return on the public investment, have given us second-rate forests in the hills.

Upland afforestation is also inextricably linked with the excessive planting target set by the government. EFG's chairman (Hansard 1988b) pointed out: 'it will on the whole be the more marginal land in the uplands that will be drawn into forestry. Indeed, if that is not so, it is again unlikely that the Government's planting targets can be met.'

Windthrow hazard classification

By examining the relationship between endemic windthrow and environmental factors, the FC was able to produce a windthrow hazard classification in 1977. This allows the likely onset of wind damage to be predicted. A series of sample sites are selected on an area of planting land, or in an established plantation, and at each site scores are given to four key factors: wind zone, topographical shelter, elevation and soil type (FC 1985).

The wind zone indicates the 'windiness' of different regions of Britain, according to the frequency and severity of strong winds. The windiest zones are in northern and western areas close to the coast. The severity of winds also increases with elevation, and a score is given to the height above sea-level obtained from Ordnance Survey maps.

Topography of the surrounding land is important because it determines the amount of shelter from the wind, and can be quantified by an assessment of topex which measures the angles to the horizon at eight points of the compass at each sample site. In a totally flat landscape there is no topographic shelter, the topex assessment is zero, and a maximum point score is added into the hazard classification. Deep valleys and glens provide the most protection from wind, but much afforestation has taken place on low rolling hills, or open moorlands such as the Flow Country, which are very exposed.

Finally, soil types are assessed. Soils which are waterlogged, or have other restrictions to rooting, score highest in the hazard classification. The totals of the four scores at each sample site are added together and the windthrow hazard class (WHC) obtained. Land or plantations which fall into WHC 6 are the most vulnerable to wind damage, and WHC 1 sites are the most stable. Hazard classes throughout an area can be used to produce a WHC map (Figure 10.4).

Effects of wind on plantation management

Hazard classes now play a vital role in upland plantation management. From them a critical height of the tree crop can be estimated, at which the trees will start to blow over. The critical height of a crop also depends on whether the trees are thinned out or left unthinned. In general, disturbance of the tree canopy by thinning makes the crop more vulnerable and the trees blow over sooner. For a thinned crop of Sitka spruce on a WHC 6 site, the critical height can be as low as 29 ft (9 m), which the trees can reach in just 15–25 years, depending on their growth rate. If the crop is left unthinned, the critical height is extended to 42 ft (13 m) and the trees can grow on for 20–35 years.

The art of modern forest management in vulnerable upland plantations now consists of attempts to keep conifer crops standing

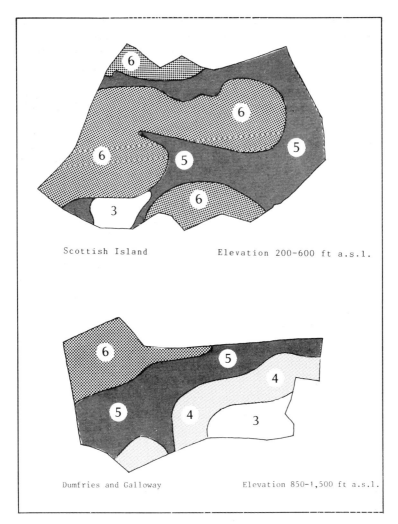

Figure 10.4 *Typical windthrow hazard class maps*

as long as possible, to produce bigger trees and improve economic returns. An inevitable consequence is that many upland forests are managed on a no-thin regime and are never thinned out, so that they remain dense, dark and virtually impenetrable throughout their shortened rotations. This has important implications for their nature conservation value, for as the NCC (1986) has pointed out, the only real means of improving the value of such crops for wildlife habitat would be to thin them.

The FC has found that losses due to wind damage in thinned plantations on WHC 5 and 6 sites 'are so grievous' that it has decided generally not to thin such crops in future (Grayson 1981). This is confirmed by W. Harper (1986): 'In general, crops on sites of wind hazard classes 5 and 6 are so prone to damage that any thinning will seriously foreshorten the rotation and greatly reduce the revenue.' Fully 35 per cent of FC crops will not now be thinned because of the economic effects of windthrow, and additional areas will not be thinned where the terrain is too steep (Rollinson 1985).

In exposed conditions, on poor land, the area of plantations that can never be thinned out is huge: 'Commonly forests in south Scotland have between 40–50 per cent of their area in WHC 5 and 6 where thinning is rarely practised. This amounts to 124,000 acres (50,000 ha) of FC land alone. Managers can therefore start to think in terms of rotations of only 35–40 years before extensive wind damage occurs in WHC 5 and 6 for yield class 12 to 14 crops' (*F&BT* May 1980).

In south Scotland and the borders WHC 3 land available for afforestation, or already planted, where tree crops could be thinned without too much worry, is rare and usually limited to lower hill slopes with well drained soils. Above this, is a zone of WHC 4 where thinning can be carried out with care, but much of a typical plantation is WHC 5 and 6 (as shown in the stylised, typical plantation in Figure 10.4). In other parts of Britain plantations or planting land may be entirely WHC 5 and 6, such as in the Flow Country, or on the islands off the Scottish coast (Figure 10.4).

Hazard classes in the Flow Country have been a subject of a heated dispute between foresters and conservationists. The RSPB (1987) carried out its own survey which placed most of the exposed bogs in WHC 5 and 6, while Fountain Forestry had claimed they were WHC 4. Under questioning by the PAC (1987), the FC acknowledged that Flow Country planting sites were generally WHC 5, with the worst being WHC 6: 'They will of course be subject to a degree of windblow but one really has to experience that to be sure about its effect.'

Respacing

The 'oceanic' system of plantation management was pioneered by the late Maj.-Gen. D.G. Moore, who thought that: 'Windthrow is not an act of god. It is the outward and visible sign of silvicultural failure' (*F&BT* November 1982). The system consists of establishing conifer crops in the normal way, but at ten to twelve years old about 60 per cent of the young trees are cut down, to leave just 400 trees per acre (1,000 per ha). No attempt is made to extract the cut trees, which are simply left to rot. No further thinning is attempted and the remaining trees are left to grow on to form a final crop which aims to provide fewer, larger and more valuable trees at clearfelling. There is great debate amongst foresters about the method, and some feel it achieves nothing that could not be done by planting at a wider spacing in the first instance.

Reducing the stocking of young plantations, to a less drastic extent than under the 'oceanic' system, has become known as respacing, and is now practised by some of the afforestation companies. One of the less appealing practices is that of chemical thinning, whereby the trees are injected with a herbicide such as glyphosate instead of being cut down. This has been carried out at Eskdalemuir forest (*F&BT* February 1985) although some foresters are worried about the pest problems that might be created by a large proportion of dying trees amongst a conifer crop.

Yield class

The growth of conifer plantations is measured in terms of yield class. This figure is related to the maximum, average rate of production of timber volume per hectare. There are, however, drawbacks to the use of yield class for assessing the value and performance of plantations. As it is a volume measurement, yield class can only be known with total accuracy at the end of a plantation's rotation. Even for a conifer crop, records of timber removed during felling and thinning must be kept over a 30 to 50 year period. In practice this is hardly possible, and the FC has largely abandoned attempts to compare actual and predicted timber yields on a routine basis. On investigating the overall financial performance of the FC the NAO (1986) concluded that: 'Record-keeping over such long periods is subject to major practical difficulties and high costs. Without such corroboration, reservations inevitably arise about the accuracy of the volume assumptions incorporated in the valuation.'

The long-term nature of forest growth means that critics of yield class estimates are likely to have to wait for decades to prove themselves right. The productivity of FC conifer crops ranges between YC 2 and 24. National averages for all conifer species for FC plantations in Scotland, England and Wales are YC 9, 10 and 11 respectively (FC 1977). But Mather and Murray (1986) found a discrepancy when they asked private forestry interests to estimate the future yield class that their new plantations in Scotland would achieve:

YC 18+   8%
YC 16–18   23%
YC 14–16   40%

Less than 12 per cent of their sample schemes reported anticipated production of less than YC 12.

The forestry lobby likes to perpetuate the myth that Britain has some of the best growing conditions for conifers in Europe and overlooks the problem of wind damage that afflicts British afforestation. Average British yields are simply compared to Scandinavian figures of YC 3–5. This line of argument is not usually extended to the equally obvious fact that trees in the tropics can grow at least five times as fast as those in Britain.

The rate of return on new planting

Most of the money needed to create a new plantation is spent in the first few years, with the NAO (1986) reporting that 50 per cent of the total costs are usually incurred in the first ten years. The figures given in Chapter 5 indicate that almost 70 per cent of the £440 per acre (£1,090 per ha) spent over this period may even be incurred in the first two years. Inevitably, this means that once trees have been planted it is 'generally financially worthwhile to maintain the plantation until it is mature and harvested' (NAO 1986).

This simple, economic common-sense, helps to elucidate the forestry lobby's unceasing campaign to get more land planted. It realises that this is the crucial battle which has to be fought, and that once the trees are in the ground the argument is won and the decision irreversible. This is why the forestry lobby has suffered its greatest anxieties over the two independent, economic assessments of its activities.

The 1972 Treasury Review sent shock waves through the forestry world when it highlighted the fact that the economic return from FC plantations was likely to range from 1 per cent on poor sites distant from markets, to about 3 per cent on good sites close to markets. At the time the yardstick for assessing public investments was a return of 10 per cent, and although the test discount rate has now been reduced to 5 per cent, afforestation still looks a poor way to spend public money. Following the Review the FC was set a target of a 3 per cent return on its new planting, which recognised the inherent limitations imposed by tree growth rates in a temperate climate, in addition to the alleged, but unquantifiable benefits to rural employment and recreation.

The NAO report, based on a study by the economic consultants PIEDA (1986) re-opened the wounds which the forestry lobby suffered in 1972. PIEDA made incisive criticisms of the inadequate structure of the FC's accounts which 'do not show the rate of return on new investment which may be low or even negative'. This is a vital conclusion, given the importance of new planting. PIEDA also drew attention to the fact that the accounts are structured so that the existing forest assets are so valued that the target rate of 3 per cent is automatically achieved. This method of accounting could be used to 'achieve' whatever target rate was desired, simply by tinkering with the theoretical asset value. Furthermore, the FC's accounts are a rolling process where all past sunk costs are simply and conveniently written off, year after year.

The great value of the PIEDA and NAO reports is that they have focused attention on the rates of return achievable by individual afforestation schemes, based on the FC's own economic models, with different combinations of hazard and yield classes. The FC has shown that 67 per cent of its total area of new planting is not expected to achieve the 3 per cent target (1977). PIEDA found that the mean return on FC planting was a mere 2.25 per cent, and that where trees had to be felled early because of windthrow danger 'the returns are extremely low – as low as 0.5 per cent'. The full implications of these derisory returns only fully strike home when it is remembered that 26 per cent of FC timber, over the last 30 years, has been affected by windthrow in precisely this way (Rollinson 1985). Nearly 40 per cent of all new FC planting is expected to earn the dismal rate of return of 1.25 per cent (NAO 1986).

Only on the very best sites in southern Britain can the most productive conifer crops achieve a 5 per cent financial return. But the FC persists in concentrating its activities on poor-quality land, in a hostile climate, at precisely the opposite end of the country. This problem looms large, as almost half of the FC's land bank of planting land is located in northern Scotland. This region also has the largest concentration of plantations in any of the FC Conservancies, with over 500,000 acres (207,000 ha) of crops. PIEDA (1986) was alarmed at the prospects for continued FC investment there, and recorded that 'valuation figures for the North Scotland Conservancy are a matter of some concern and merit further investigation'.

The FC's rate of return on its new planting demands an explanation of just what it is trying to achieve. A convenient retreat is to explain that it is working to provide employment, largely for its own staff, in deprived rural areas. Another tactic is to put part of the blame for low returns onto such minimal concessions as are made to landscape and wildlife: 'If broadleaves are used or if larch is used or if boundaries are varied, all these express themselves in a slight diminution of the volume of timber production' (PAC 1987). Given that most recent FC planting up to 1986 has consisted of less than 1 per cent of broadleaves this seems a rather slim excuse.

The real reason for planting poor land goes right to the heart of the afforestation industry that has developed since 1919. It is simply because nothing else has been possible under the existing structures, targets and incentives, and an industry has been created that resists change. The PAC suggested the question that so much afforestation had taken place 'that it is now quite a difficult matter to find land on which to plant trees at anything like a reasonable rate of return'.

In the face of so much criticism of its activities the FC 'pointed out that it is now very selective in acquiring land and would not normally bid for land where investment would have a rate of return as low as 1.25 per cent' (NAO 1986). Yet this laudable, new-found discrimination does not seem to extend to the FC's role as Forestry Authority, where it continues to clear impoverished land for private afforestation with the benefit of FC grant aid.

Growing monocultures

Apart from its inability to achieve anything but the afforestation of poor-quality land, the failure of Britain's forestry policy is most clearly seen in the dreary, monocultural nature of upland plantations. In the year to March 1986 very low proportions of broadleaves were planted in Scottish afforestation schemes, with 1.01 per cent achieved by the FC and 1.4 per cent by the private sector (FC 1986a). By March 1987 the FC had boosted its own performance to just over 5 per cent broadleaves in its afforestation throughout Britain, in line with its own newly-established guidelines. The amount of broadleaves in private Scottish afforestation in the same year remained at 1.4 per cent, although the figure is likely to be an underestimate because ribbons of broadleaved planting within conifer plantations are likely to have been separately grant aided, and statistically recorded, under the Broadleaved Woodland Grant Scheme (BWGS) (FC 1987d).

The diversity of tree species is partly limited by the very poor quality of the exposed uplands that are planted. Only conifers can achieve any worthwhile timber production on such sites, where broadleaves are unavoidably ornamental concessions planted in an attempt to appease environmentalists. At Eskdalemuir the plantations established between 1966 and 1978 were 80 per cent

Sitka spruce, 19 per cent other conifers, and just 1 per cent broadleaves (EFG undated).

Even the number of conifer species which can survive in the uplands is limited, and one tree, the Sitka spruce, has proved so superior to other conifers that it has become almost synonymous with upland afforestation in Britain. It has sharp, unpalatable needles that deter grazing by livestock, withstands exposure well, and produces crops with a much higher standing volume of timber than most other commonly planted conifers. Sitka spruce, introduced from the west coast of North America, now occupies 28 per cent of all Britain's woodland, covering nearly 1.3 million acres (526,000 ha) or over 2,000 sq miles of land (FC 1987b).

Most worrying, is the way in which the predominance of Sitka spruce is continuing to increase, and it occupies an increasingly greater proportion of all new planting (Table 10.1). Mather and Murray (1986) confirm this in their survey of Scottish afforestation schemes. In 62 per cent of their sample schemes, over 80 per cent was planted with Sitka spruce, and in 92 per cent of cases there was more than 40 per cent Sitka.

The dominance of Sitka spruce would be even greater were it not for the planting of up to 50 per cent lodgepole pine in the north

Figure 10.5 *The regimented lines of blanket afforestation at Eskdalemuir in south Scotland*

Table 10.1: *The increasing dominance of Sitka spruce in Forestry Commission afforestation since 1961*

	Sitka spruce as a percentage of the total area of afforestation	
By FC conservancies –	*1961–70*	*1971–80*
North Scotland	35	57
East Scotland	30	52
West Scotland	73	88
South Scotland	62	84
North-East England	29	61
North-West England	21	40
North Wales	62	71
South Wales	51	63
By country –		
Scotland	50	68
England	14	30
Wales	57	68
Overall –		
Great Britain	38	68

Source: Forestry Commission (1984)

of Scotland, and the use of Scots pine in the east of Scotland. Lodgepole pine was once a very fashionable tree for foresters to plant but it soon became apparent that its vulnerability to deer, insects, windthrow, and poor timber quality held serious drawbacks. It is now the forester's tree of last resort, planted where conditions are so bad that even Sitka struggles. It is widely used as a 'nurse crop' to support the growth of Sitka on the most difficult sites such as the Flow Country.

Periodically, the afforestation industry's dependence on one, or at most two species of conifers is questioned:

'Sir Ralph Verney wondered whether "monocultural" practices – such as the widespread planting of Sitka spruce and lodgepole pine in the Scottish highlands – did not present a hazard in that a disease affecting one species could result in wholesale deaths in forestry plantations' (*F&BT* May 1978).

Dr Malcolm at Edinburgh University also warned that 'the extent of the reliance placed on one species . . . may be unwise' (*F&BT* October 1979). Rowan (1986) thought that: 'The great success of

Sitka spruce has raised the question of whether we now rely on it, and to a lesser extent lodgepole pine, overmuch.'

Such doubts, from the evidence of state and private afforestation practice, have little effect. It seems inevitable that an even greater future reliance is to be placed on Sitka spruce as the dominant crop of upland afforestation. The earliest plantations were clearly more diverse, but are not likely to stay that way (Ogilvy 1986):

'Many of our existing forests are planted with much more specific attention to ground variation, so that we see Sitka spruce in the flushes, lodgepole pine on the blanket peats, Scots pine and European larch on the mineral heaths, Norway spruce on the drier grass lands, and Douglas fir, hemlock fir or cypress on the brown forest earths. Many of these, particularly lodgepole pines on peat, will be replaced by Sitka spruce after clearfelling.'

This threat of increased dependence on Sitka is a reality in the FC's proposals for the management of its Kielder Forest for 1986–90. Sitka spruce is proposed to increase from 70 per cent to 82 per cent, while Norway spruce will be cut from 15 to 3 per cent, with the 10 per cent of lodgepole pine disappearing altogether (FC 1986c).

The hope of some academics that the second rotation of conifer crops in the uplands would be more diverse are clearly going to be dashed. The FC's own *Guide to Upland Restocking* (1985b) states that: 'In most circumstances, Sitka spruce is likely to be the first choice for replanting in upland forests'. R.C. Steele and Dr J. Balfour foresaw that: 'Most new forests will be planted with Sitka spruce except in the most difficult sites where lodgepole pine was (until pine beauty moth appeared) the preferred species. There is unlikely to be any significant species switch in the second rotation' (*F&BT* October 1979).

The development of processing industries to take up the supply of Sitka spruce, which is particularly suitable for paper making, only serves to reinforce the dominance of the tree. About 90 per cent of the wood intake into the Shotton mill will be spruce. The Scandinavian consultants, Jaakko Poyry, reported to the FC that consideration should be given to restricting the proportion of larch being planted, because this was less suitable for pulp manufacturing (*F&BT* June 1980). Such pressures will make it even more difficult for the FC to attempt to make cosmetic gestures to landscape its plantations, where larch has an important role as a deciduous conifer. Larch can also create plantations which, arguably, are slightly more beneficial to wildlife, as the tree does not cast such a heavy shade and allows the development of a ground flora.

Insect pests – the pine beauty moth

Agricultural crops, grown in large, monocultural, even-aged blocks, and with a uniform genetic structure, have proved vulnerable to serious damage by pests and diseases. Blanket afforestation creates the ideal conditions for such problems to develop in today's tree crops. Extensive damage was caused to crops of lodgepole pine in the late-1970s by the pine beauty moth (*Panolis flammea*), a handsome insect with ochreous brown wings with a reddish tinge. It had previously lived in harmony with its native food plant, the Scots pine, but has adapted to feed on the vast new plantations of lodgepole pine. Its caterpillars build up to such great numbers on these trees that they are completely stripped of their needles and killed.

The problem began in the FC's plantations in the Flow Country, where an FC spokesman noted that: 'Lodgepole pine is so far the only tree species found able to grow successfully in these northern conditions of high exposure and poor acid peats'; the infestation of the moth's caterpillars was so great that it threatened FC planting policy in north Scotland (*F&BT* August/September 1978). During 1976 and 1977 about 600 acres (240 ha) of lodgepole pine were destroyed in the FC's plantations at Naver in the Flow Country, and it soon became apparent that tens of thousands of acres were at risk, including areas in east and south Scotland.

Foresters have had to respond by aerial applications of the insecticide fenitrothion, and between 1977 and 1986 at least 37,000 acres (15,000 ha) of vulnerable crops were sprayed, including almost 12,000 acres (4,700 ha) in 1985 alone (NCC 1986). Environmentalists fear the development of the 'treadmill' effect of pesticide dependence, as in parts of North America, where repeated spraying is routine forest management. The introduction of aerial pesticide techniques, together with fertiliser applications, is an unforgivable intrusion into areas of largely undisturbed, semi-natural habitat such as the Flow Country, and a sad reflection on the policies that have allowed afforestation to take place there.

It is likely that the development of pest problems in the Flow Country is linked to the difficult site conditions and environmental stresses which lead to poor growth of the trees. It is fortunate for the forestry lobby that the Flow Country is so remote, as public oppositon to aerial pesticide applications would have been greater if they had been proposed in the more densely populated areas of England or Wales. There would also have been much more concern about the trial release of genetically engineered viruses, which has also occurred in the Flow Country, in an attempt to control the pine beauty moth. The lack of comment and opposition to this is in marked contrast to the North American experience.

Figure 10.6 *Whole swathes of lodgepole pine are stripped of their needles and killed by the caterpillars of the pine beauty moth, leaving the bleached skeletons of the trees, at a Forestry Commission plantation in the Flow Country. Foresters have had to resort to aerial applications of insecticide*

It is likely that other insects, native to Britain, will eventually turn their attention to the new food supplies of alien conifers that are being provided for them. Existing pests include pine looper, pine shoot moth, winter moth, pine weevil, black pine beetles, pine sawfly and green spruce aphis. The European spruce sawfly (*Gilpinia hercyniae*) is found throughout England and Wales, but not

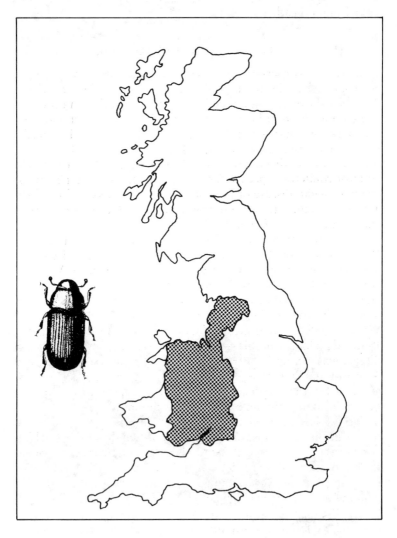

Figure 10.7 *Great spruce bark beetle – areas where movement of spruce timber is controlled by licence*   Source: Forestry Commission 1985c

yet in Scotland, and 'presents a serious threat to the extensive upland spruce plantations in Britain' (FC 1979). The vapourer moth (*Orgyia antiqua*) is often found feeding on lodgepole pine and Sitka spruce in Scotland, and several small outbreaks of pest proportions have been noted. There is speculation that such outbreaks are 'an indication of less than healthy tree growth', and that they may predispose the crop to attack by other insects such as the pine beauty moth (Leather 1986).

The great spruce bark beetle

To date, the most serious insect pest to threaten Sitka spruce, is the great spruce bark beetle (*Dendroctonus micans*). Unlike the insects described above, it is not a native species, but has been introduced unintentionally from Europe where it is a serious pest in Holland, Denmark and north-west Germany. It is a wood-boring beetle, whose larvae feed below the bark of conifers and can kill the trees. Although the beetle mainly attacks Sitka spruce, it has been found on most coniferous species. Again it seems that trees under stress, due to drought, disease or poor soil, are most at risk; a fact which has serious implications for a programme of afforestation on poor quality sites (*F&BT* September 1982).

It is likely that the beetle first became established in Britain in 1973, but because of its inconspicuous habits it was not discovered until 1982 when outbreaks were found in Shropshire. Much of Wales and the borders with England have now been found to be affected. The initial reaction of the FC in 1982 was: 'This is not a serious outbreak and bears no comparison with Dutch elm disease. We are confident that we can stamp it out' (*F&BT* September 1982). With hindsight this seems a complacent view, but once again the FC was clearly hamstrung by its conflicting roles of Forestry Authority and Enterprise. These forced it to understate the potential problem, for fear of reducing the confidence that sustains the investment needed to maintain blanket afforestation.

The FC has imposed restrictions on the movement of spruce timber throughout most of Wales and bordering areas of England (see Figure 10.7). The beetle has a high, natural capacity for spread to new locations (Evans 1984a), and there is a gradual expansion of its territory to the west, although spread to the north and east is inhibited by urban development (King and Fielding 1987). Hugh Evans (1984b) has warned that: 'Most spruce in Britain remains at risk and we must be ready for movement of the beetle into new areas where its effects may well be more serious, especially in large stands of mature Sitka spruce.'

═ 11 ═
Lowland Forestry – the Lost Tradition

The decline of lowland forestry

It is a depressing reflection on the state of British forestry that the FC Annual Report for 1986/87, referring to an increase in the afforestation target to 81,500 acres (33,000 ha), described this as 'traditional' forestry. This is a none too subtle piece of propaganda by the forestry lobby, attempting to improve the public image of the conifer plantations which have dominated such planting, relegating the smaller, more diverse woodlands of the lowlands further into obscurity. Such lowland woodlands, which may have been shaped by the activities of man for hundreds or thousands of years, are the true inheritors of forestry tradition, yet they have been shamefully neglected and inadequately protected by national forest policies. Many were ravaged by the fellings of the First and Second World Wars, but attempts to replant or regenerate them became subverted into the drive to afforest the uplands with conifers.

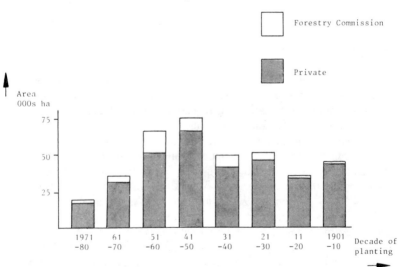

Figure 11.1 *The age structure of Britain's broadleaved woodlands in 1980*   Source: Forestry Commission 1987b

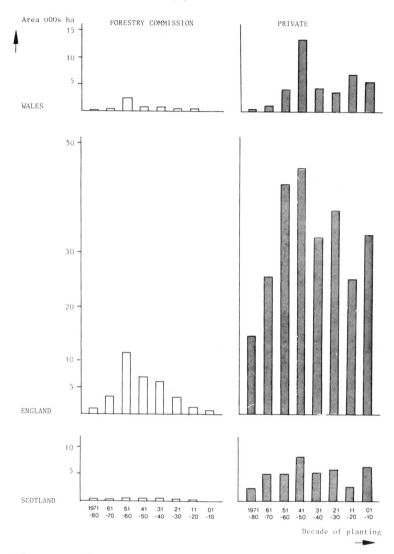

Figure 11.2 *The age structure of broadleaved woodlands in Wales, England and Scotland in 1980*   Source: Forestry Commission 1987b

The problem at the heart of British forestry is the gulf that has grown between these two facets of forestry practice. Whilst the blanket afforestation of the uplands boomed, the amount of new broadleaved planting and restocking throughout Britain steadily declined. Figures 11.1 and 11.2 show the age structure of woodlands mostly composed of broadleaves, as surveyed by the FC between 1979 and 1982. It can be seen that broadleaved restocking and planting peaked in the decade 1941–1950, but collapsed thereafter. The FC's own lamentable contribution is striking. The majority of broadleaved planting has been carried out by private interests in England, where there is a larger area of land suitable for growing such trees, but even this has progressively diminished.

The disparity between conifer and broadleaved planting has persisted despite the introduction of much higher grants for planting broadleaves. Blanket conifer planting flourished purely and simply because of tax avoidance. It was carried out on cheap land in the hills, by absentee owners who relied on the sale of a large plantation to a financial institution to make a return on their investment.

Tax avoidance could not be exploited so profitably by the owners of smaller woodlands in the lowlands, who operate under an entirely different set of objectives and circumstances. These often involve the ownership of scattered woodlands as part of a mixed estate or farm. Ownership tends to be long-term, handed down through a family, and sales to some form of secondary market would be impracticable or even impossible. Some owners of traditional, landed estates were able to offset the costs of maintaining their woodlands under Schedule D, and to transfer ownership of parts of their holdings to other members of the family to obtain tax-free income under Schedule B when the trees matured. Such owners are very influential in the TGUK. But many other woodland owners such as farmers and other individuals on lower incomes, derived little or no benefit from tax avoidance.

The problems of growing broadleaves

In Britain's upland hills and moors, land used for rough grazing has only a low agricultural value, determined by the number of sheep it will support. The afforestation industry, supported by much greater subsidies per unit area of land, was able to pay a much higher price for the same land. A forestry land price spiral was created in the uplands, as described in Chapter 5, which sustained blanket afforestation.

Unfortunately, afforestation in the lowlands has precisely the opposite effect, and a pernicious, reverse land price spiral is created. In the lowlands the price of agricultural land rose steadily after the Second World War, and has only partially declined in recent years. The price of arable farmland commonly reached £2,000–3,000 per acre (£5,000–7,400 per ha). When trees are planted on such land its price instantly plummets, to perhaps just £300–500 per acre (£750–1,250 per ha). This simple fact creates an extremely difficult obstacle, which has to be overcome before substantial planting of trees in the lowlands can take place.

Other difficulties associated with lowland forestry must also be faced. Traditionally, farm woodlands are small and scattered, and many farms might have just 2–15 acres (1–6 ha) of tree cover. This means that economies of scale are not possible, and items such as fencing, needed repeatedly through the rotation of the trees, are very expensive. Access to such woodlands often means a long journey across fields which also reduces timber values. Broadleaved trees, such as the oak, beech and ash that we all associate with lowland forestry, generally produce timber at only one half or one third of the rate of an average crop of conifers. Young broadleaved trees are also more expensive to buy than conifers, and are more vulnerable to damage by deer, livestock and squirrels. Lowland forestry is also bedevilled by the high costs of the repeated weeding needed to control competing vegetation on fertile sites.

A report by a CLA (1986) working party summed up the problems faced by landowners wishing to invest in forestry on their own land. It is such people who bear the burden of maintaining lowland, broadleaved woodlands, so their concerns are particularly relevant:

'It must be faced that for many landowners the economics of forestry simply do not add up. For them the undertaking of a new forestry enterprise, in particular, is not economically possible . . . Without a radical change in the policies and support mechanisms for the major land uses, farming and forestry, and continuing improvements in markets and market prices, for timber and timber products, landowners are unlikely to invest . . .'

Of course, the economies of upland afforestation by absentee owners do not add up either, without massive subsidies offered through tax avoidance or grants.

Problems of managing lowland woodlands

Routine management of existing small woodlands in the lowlands is affected by similar problems. Even when such tree crops are fully grown, the combined value of the trees and the land on which they stand is often less than the agricultural value of adjoining farmland. A typical, average quality woodland, with trees that might be over 100 years old, might be worth just £500–1,000 per acre (£1,250–2,500 per ha). Following the Second World War, the low value of woodlands in comparison to farmland, led to many being cleared for agriculture. Others were simply neglected because the costs of essential management work were too high in relation to the potential returns. The CLA (1986) know what is wrong:

'The substantial acreage of unmanaged private woodlands, and conversion to agricultural land, testify to the inability of these woodlands to produce a profitable crop. Widespread exploitation of woodlands during the two World Wars reduced their potential to yield timber of any value, and without the capital required to rehabilitate exploited crops, many woodlands have been left to fall into neglect.'

Matters are not helped by the structure of the FC grant schemes, which emphasise the provision of planting grants rather than grants to encourage routine management. Management grants were a feature of the dedication schemes, but their value was steadily eroded, and they were not continued when the FGS replaced dedication. The change towards planting, rather than management grants, was also a reflection of the corruption of the dedication scheme, which although intended as a means of restocking mainly broadleaved woodlands, became the vehicle for new planting of conifers in the uplands.

The simplified FGS consisted of the straightforward payment of planting grants, and a main consideration was to reduce the costs of administration. The BWGS and the WGS which followed, have adopted the same format. The failure of such grant schemes adequately to encourage woodland management is clearly shown by their co-existence with 420,000 acres (170,000 ha) of 'unproductive' woodland. This consists of felled land awaiting replanting and scrub woodland of little value for timber (FC 1987 f). The area is more than five times the current annual afforestation target in the uplands, and it is a pity that the forestry lobby has not shown more concern about encouraging appropriate management of this neglected resource. Once again the CLA (1986) is aware of the problem:

'Other shortcomings include the overemphasis on planting rather than continuing management, and the lack of income restoration for farmers converting land, during the first 15–20 years of establishment. The discontinued dedication schemes incorporated long-term planning and management provisions related to grant payments and regular supervision. Some form of these should be restored.'

The fate of ancient semi-natural woodlands

Lowland broadleaved woodlands often have a high value for wildlife and conservation, and ancient semi-natural woodlands are particularly important in this respect. They are defined as having been continuously wooded since the year 1600 and are characterised by native tree species with a range of age classes, including old and dead trees, and a varied structure with open glades. The plant and animal communities which have developed in such woods over hundreds, or even thousands of years, are especially rich.

These wonderful woodlands were also the victims of conversion to agriculture or coniferisation. Their area in England and Wales has declined by 30 to 50 per cent since 1945 because of such practices, with the extent of the losses ranging from 24 per cent in Essex to 63 per cent in Shropshire (NCC 1984). On a more positive note, the growing public realisation of the destruction of ancient woodlands, and the outcry that ensued, did much to propel the FC into a review of its broadleaved policy which resulted in significant improvements.

The view from the forestry lobby

The forestry lobby showed little concern about the fate of small woodlands, as it became increasingly preoccupied with the upland afforestation industry. Broadleaved forestry quickly became a poor relation, with all the money and career glamour to be made in the uplands. The number of owners of small woodlands amongst the ranks of the TGUK declined, as this lobby group became increasingly dominated by interests associated with upland afforestation.

EFG (1985 c) acknowledge the decline in broadleaved planting since the Second World War and point to the lower quality of broadleaved woodlands and the associated management problems:

'If large areas of very high quality hardwood plantations could be acquired relatively cheaply and squirrels, which can seriously damage the bark of trees, were to be controlled more positively, then there might be a case for institutions to acquire more hardwoods. Unfortunately the total area of broadleaved woodland in Britain is limited . . . it is extremely difficult to find properties of sufficient size with good quality . . .'

The mainstream forestry lobby concerned itself so narrowly with the upland afforestation industry, that conservationists' anxieties about the state of lowland woodlands came to be seen as a threat, generated by public pressure, as reported at the APF conference:

'It is a matter of concern for foresters to learn of the very considerable and dominating influence that the Nature Conservancy could impose on the Forest Authority where population densities resulted in extreme pressure on land use' (*F&BT* June/July 1978).

Such public pressure was seen as an attempt to dictate to the forestry lobby. A Small Woods Scheme of planting grants was introduced to encourage tree planting on a smaller scale than was possible under dedication: 'Foresters, however, must not forget that the Small Woods Scheme was introduced largely as a result of pressures from "amenity" interests and that too great a disregard of their representations could lead to the administration of the grant being taken out of the FC's hands' (*F&BT* June/July 1978).

The defence of tax avoidance

The forestry lobby was severely inhibited from putting forward any realistic proposals to help manage small, broadleaved woodlands, for fear of upsetting the fragile system of tax avoidance that sustained blanket afforestation in the uplands. It was clear that tax avoidance did little to help many small woods, but the lobby did not want any move towards a system of grants which might threaten the basis of upland planting.

Grove (1983) quotes the FC director-general:

'I fully agree with those who have said that it is hard to imagine broadleaved woodlands and broadleaved investment being attractive to financial institutions – we have to look mainly at the individual owner and at a package of benefits that would motivate him. As a result of considerable efforts by many parties, we have income tax benefits associated with forestry, together with what I believe to be a not ungenerous level of support.'

A CLA (1986) working party confirmed that tax avoidance, together with FC planting grants, had certainly achieved planting of a 'significant scale' in the uplands. At the same time it realised that farmers, on relatively low incomes, would not be able to benefit from tax avoidance as an incentive to plant trees. The working party report concluded 'there was little to be achieved for the smaller investor or farmer through amendment of the taxation system'. Unsurprisingly, the report went on to protect the upland afforestation industry: 'Nor was any reason seen for disturbing the existing arrangements for those that it does encourage into forestry. Indeed, the dangers of undermining confidence in long-term investment by changing the rules, were stressed. The Government target for planting is not being met and the taxation arrangements are a major attraction for investment in forestry. It is vital that this source of private investment funding in the rural areas is not curtailed by interference with the fiscal incentives.'

The role of the Forestry Authority

The FC has presided over the coniferisation, clearance and neglect of lowland woodlands since the Second World War. Until recently it took the narrow view that it had to support coniferisation, as a productive silvicultural method, rather than insisting on continued broadleaved management. This was clearly shown in an FC reply to the question: 'Is it positively your policy to refuse permission to plant evergreens after felling broadleaves?' posed by a House of Lords Committee in 1982. Grove (1983) records the FC reply:

'It is very hard to generalise in answer to that. Our policy in our own areas is clear, but when it comes to the criteria in the case of private applicants, if they insist on doing something which is acceptable in silvicultural terms, in terms of the prospect of producing merchantable timber, it is hard for us to say no.'

In particular, the FC condoned the loss of up to 60 per cent of ancient semi-natural woodland in parts of Britain, partly through taking a blinkered approach to what constituted sound, economic forestry practice. Grove (1983) described how serious the position had become by the early 1980s:

'Most conservation bodies, including the NCC find the apparent inability of the FC to indicate any more commitment to the protection of Britain's woodlands extraordinary in view of the urgency of the situation and the continuing rapid destruction of woodland habitats.'

Grove (1983) highlighted another of the FC's disturbing failures:

'One outstanding difficulty in ensuring the survival of ancient woodlands is the failure in recent Forestry Commission censuses to distinguish ancient woodland from broadleaved plantations, a distinction which one would expect to be made in view of the conservation remit of the FC. In fact this appears to be a quite deliberate omission to sidestep the whole issue of the present high level of ancient woodland erosion by maintaining that the area of "broadleaved" woodland is stable.'

The reluctance of the FC to respond adequately to public opinion and conservation pressure led to a disastrous public image for the forestry profession. By the time that the FC had revised its broadleaved policies, and announced the BWGS, the damage had been done. The achievements of the conservationists' pressure was clear: 'It has brought the Forestry Commission to the very, very belated recognition that lowland woods should be hardwood (broadleaved) in character which view that much-beloved body is about to force feed upon the rest of the industry' (*F & BT* December 1984).

The FC has also been trapped by its dual role, where the economic stringencies of the Forestry Enterprise contributed to a withdrawal and distancing from its expensive and time consuming role of Forestry Authority and to a vacuum in the provision of sound forestry advice. This has been variously filled by a whole range of other interests including agricultural departments, the NCC, local authorities, the RSPB, the Countryside Commission and the National Parks. Confusion amongst farmers and others seeking advice is the obvious result. As the CLA (1986) remarked:

'The variety of schemes and the specificity of purpose for each are both confusing and irrational. If woodlands are to meet the multiplicity of purposes discussed earlier, then it would be logical for there to be a rationalised system of grants and related advice.'

The Broadleaved Woodland Grant Scheme

In the face of growing concern about the depletion and neglect of lowland woodlands, the FC set about a two year revision of its broadleaved policy, resulting in new guidelines and the announcement of the BWGS in 1985. This was a breakthrough for conservation in several respects. The FC at last recognised that grants were needed to encourage the planting and management of broadleaved woodlands whose primary purpose was for amenity and conservation, and timber production no longer had to be the overriding priority. Grants were also made available for the sole purpose of planting pure broadleaves, and were about 40 per cent higher than previously available. Most importantly, presumptions were established that broadleaved woodlands were to remain broadleaved in character, and that they were not to be reclaimed for agriculture. The felling licence controls which had formerly allowed woodlands to be progressively, and perfectly legally, felled, were also tightened considerably.

The BWGS proved to be short-lived because of further changes to the FC grant schemes in the wake of the 1988 Budget, but it enjoyed success in several ways. There were 5,200 applications to enter the scheme in the first 15 months, involving over 91,000 acres (37,000 ha) of land (FC 1987 d). Just over half of the work actually carried out under the scheme in the year to March 1987 consisted of restocking in existing woodlands rather than new planting on bare land.

Certainly, difficulties and doubts about some aspects of the scheme were beginning to emerge. It was clear that long-term management was still not being adequately addressed, management objectives contained in schemes were often so vague as to be meaningless, and there was no legally binding obligation on owners to continue to comply with the scheme. The FC could also be seen to be distancing itself still further from its Authority role, leaving the job of preparing plans of operations to consultants and other advisers, making a token £100 grant available to them to do the job, as a temporary stimulus.

The Woodland Grant Scheme

The BWGS and the FGS closed to new applicants on 15 March 1988. The closure of the tax loophole in the Budget meant that a new way of financing upland conifer afforestation had to be found to appease the forestry lobby. This was achieved by merging the two former grant schemes, to form the WGS, and by massively increasing the grant for planting pure blocks of conifers, to over 250 per cent of its former level. This increase in the levels of grant to protect the upland afforestation industry, had a beneficial side-effect for lowland woodlands, because the grants for smaller planting schemes were pushed up as well. This can only be welcomed, but the impetus behind the achievement is perverse, having more to do with compensation for the loss of tax avoidance than a recognition of the needs of broadleaved woodlands. The WGS has also increased the incentives for planting mixtures of conifers and broadleaves which is a concession to considerable pressure from the TGUK.

The agricultural surpluses debate

The hills and moors of the uplands are mostly farmed using low-intensity systems of sheep grazing. The amount of subsidy received by hill farmers, in relation to the area of land they manage, and in comparison to their counterparts in the lowlands, is low. There is no 'mountain' of surplus mutton produced by hill farmers, and foresters recognise that upland farmers contribute little to the widely publicised excesses of agricultural production. Rowan (1986) wrote of the change from agricultural use to forestry in the uplands: 'This smooth transition, moreover, has caused minimal reduction in agricultural output, even in those areas where expansion has been greatest.'

Taylor (1987 a) thinks that commercial conifer production in the west and north 'will have a negligible effect on agricultural production'. Mather and Murray (1986) quantified the very limited effects of upland afforestation on farm output. In over half of the sample cases they studied in Scotland, there was no reduction in sheep numbers on a farm after partial afforestation. In a further 20 per cent of cases there was a reduction of less than 100 ewes, and more than 500 ewes were lost in only 6 per cent of cases studied. These effects arise from the sale of the poorest grazing land from a farm, in the first instance, which is clearly in the interests of the farmer if he or she continues to farm the remainder. The former DAFS policy of retaining better land in agriculture has also contributed. The researchers did find some evidence of a tendency for sheep losses caused by forestry to be greater in those regions which were already widely afforested. This would seem to be an inevitable consequence of all of the less productive farmland being steadily planted, followed by forestry taking over the better farmland.

The fact that blanket upland afforestation does not significantly reduce farm production does not deter the forestry lobby from making propaganda use of the growing public realisation of agricultural surpluses. Lobbyists speak of the need to take farmland out of production, and the pressure that they were able to bring to bear on DAFS led to restrictions on the afforestation of better hill land in Scotland being scrapped (see Chapter 9). Facts become unimportant in a propaganda battle, and the forestry lobby was able to make skilful use of a tide of feeling against farm overproduction.

The NCC (1986) foresaw what the defeat of DAFS would mean for the upland countryside of Scotland:

'The recent (March 1986) relaxation of agricultural clearance criteria in Scotland will lead to an extension of new planting onto better hill and marginal land, so that forestry will move "down the hill" though it will not expand onto better grade lower ground, especially arable. The further presumption in favour of forestry in hill areas where the land is unimproved or not capable of making a significant agricultural contribution will facilitate the expansion of afforestation within semi-natural moorland and blanket bog. These changes have quite serious implications for the still wider attrition of upland habitats, yet do nothing to alleviate the problems of farming surpluses in the lowlands of England.'

The Farm Woodlands Scheme

The annual payments of the FWS are a tacit recognition of the failure of previous grant schemes to provide sufficient incentives for broadleaved planting. It is unfortunate that the momentum for increased lowland forestry has come, not from any realisation of its intrinsic worth for wildlife or landscape, but from the unrelated economic and political necessities of attempting to reduce subsidised farm production.

The problem of agricultural surpluses caused by intensive, lowland farming led to a search by the government for alternative land uses. The resulting proposals, known by the acronym ALURE, put forward incentives for lowland tree planting by farmers at the end of 1987. After consultation these were increased to the levels shown in Table 11.1.

Table 11.1: *The Farm Woodland Scheme*

1. PLANTING GRANTS FOR BROADLEAVES AND CONIFERS

Area approved for planting or regeneration in hectares	RATE OF GRANT	
	Conifers (old FGS rates) £ per ha	Broadleaves (new WGS rates) £ per ha
0.25 – 0.9	£630	£1,575
1.0 – 2.9	£505	£1,375
3.0 – 9.9	£420	£1,175
10 and over	£240	£ 975

1 ha = 2.471 acres

2. ANNUAL PAYMENTS FOR 20, 30 OR 40 YEARS

planting on lowland farms	– £190 per ha
planting in disadvantaged areas	– £150 per ha
planting in severely disadvantaged areas	– £100 per ha
planting on marginal land and rough grazing in less favoured areas	– £ 30 per ha

40 year payments apply to planting pure oak or beech

30 year payments apply to planting of more than 50% broadleaves

20 year payments apply to other planting

The FWS employs the WGS grants, except that the conifer planting grant remains at the level of the old FGS, and was not increased in line with its counterpart for broadleaves. Most importantly, farmers are to receive annual payments for 20, 30 or 40 years, according to the proportion of broadleaves planted, until their tree crops start to produce timber. The maximum annual payment will be £77 per acre (£190 per ha) to lowland farmers. The scheme is clearly targeted at arable and improved grasslands, and an upper limit of around 89,000 acres (36,000 ha) can be grant aided during the first three years of operation from the autumn of 1988. Farmers who participate must also plant a minimum of 7.4 acres (3 ha) over the three years, in areas that are a minimum of 2.5 acres (1 ha) in size.

The success of the incentives will depend in large measure on the ability of the annual payments to overcome the problem of the reverse land price spiral described above. It is likely that payments at the existing level will only encourage farmers to afforest land that has an agricultural value of £1,000 per acre (£2,500 per ha) or less. There is also no deep tradition of forestry management by farmers in Britain, as this has always been an activity carried out by landlords. A lot will depend on how much the interest and imagination of farmers can be captured.

Reactions from the forestry lobby

Throughout the agricultural surpluses debate the forestry lobby has been extremely concerned to protect the upland afforestation industry, and it has enjoyed a great success in achieving this. The target set for lowland planting under the FWS is seen by the government to be additional to the existing afforestation target of 81,500 acres (33,000 ha) of planting. In this respect, a passage from the NCC's *Nature Conservation and Afforestation* (1986) proved ominously prescient: 'This is a *prima facie* indication that the possible future afforestation of good lowland farmland will be regarded as an *addition* and not as a substitute to existing forestry programmes.' This is precisely what the forestry lobby has succeeded in accomplishing.

The forestry lobby has also sought to emphasise that 'penny packet' lowland planting must not interfere with the grand design of upland afforestation. This was clearly a theme adopted by a spokesman for the TGUK:

'He gave warning that there could be a great deal of confusion in future forestry developments. There were two totally separate elements: a national commercial forestry policy concerned with import substitution, job creation and adding value; and an EEC agricultural surplus problem with the consequent need to take land out of farm production, leading to some interest in farm forestry' (*Scotsman* 17 December 1986).

Part Four

Freeing the Hills

═ 12 ═

Arguing Against
the Forestry Lobby

The CAS Report

The government's conversion to afforestation to save imports, which is really nothing more than a refined version of the case for providing a strategic reserve of timber, can be traced back to the CAS report of 1980. This attempted to predict the world supply and demand for timber up to the year 2025. Demand for timber was assumed to be directly linked to economic growth and income per head of population, and it was forecast that supply would fall 32 per cent short of demand by 2025. At the same time timber prices were estimated to rise by 30 to 150 per cent relative to other prices. Any such forecasting is, as the report itself admitted 'fraught with problems'. Although the report is now taken less seriously, especially in the wake of the independent study by PIEDA (1986), it is still referred to, although more cautiously than before, as shown by Williams (1984): 'In 1980 the report for the CAS forecast that by the year 2000 there was likely to be an overall deficit of 10 per cent in total supply. The projection has sometimes been disputed but the very difference of opinion proves at least that the future is uncertain and if there is a deficit we cannot afford to have been wrong.'

The cost of imports

The forestry lobby is deeply preoccupied with the value of timber imported into Britain. Almost every edition of *Forestry and British Timber* carries some reference to a soaring import bill, and a forester is invariably at hand to emphasise the need for further afforestation and increased home production:

TIMBER IMPORTS BILL SOARS AGAIN IN 1978
'The United Kingdom imported £2,370 million worth of timber and timber products in 1978 ... equivalent to over £1 million per working hour. "This is an astronomical outlay ... the bill for 1979 could well exceed £2,500 million ... Private owners have the land and labour available and all they require is a firm lead from

the government and freedom from the constraints that have undermined confidence in the past" ' (M. Harley, TGO president, *F & BT* June 1979).

IMPORTS SOARED TO £4.5 BILLION IN 1985

'Brian Howell of Fountain Forestry commented . . . "New British paper and board mills and sawmills will require increasing quantities of small roundwood and sawlogs . . . to reduce the inevitable balance-of-payments deficit . . ." ' (*F & BT* May 1985).

IMPORTS UP £346 MILLION

'The timber import bill up from £4.543 billion to £4.889 billion underlines the wisdom of the government's decision to increase home planting targets by 10 per cent a year, Brian Howell, a director of Fountain Forestry commented' (*F & BT* May 1987).

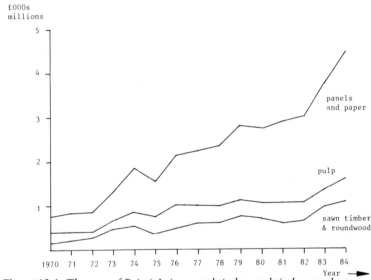

Figure 12.1 *The cost of Britain's imported timber and timber products*
Source: Department of Trade and Industry Overseas Statistics

The cost of timber and timber products imported into Britain since 1965 is shown in Figure 12.1, and the soaring bill, beloved of the forestry lobby is clearly illustrated. But the figures take no account of inflation, or of the strength of the pound relative to other currencies which has a crucial effect on the cost of imports. Norman (1980) has taken a wider view of the issues, and has assessed the contribution of timber imports to the UK's entire import bill over 18 years:

'Between 1960 and 1978 the value of forest products has fallen sharply as a proportion of the total import bill. In 1960 about 10 per cent of UK imports were forest products and in 1978 the figure was only 5.8 per cent. Over this period the value of imports of forest products increased by 423.8 per cent compared with 844.5 per cent for other goods. All UK exports increased by 838.5 per cent over the same period. It can be seen that forest products imports relative to other imports have fallen over the period 1960–78 by a sizeable 45 per cent.'

It is clear that timber is becoming a progressively less important import into Britain. The total value of timber imports is now fourth behind the value of imported vehicles, food and fuel (Figure 12.2). There is a conspicuous lack of political support for subsidies to help other British manufacturing industries, such as vehicle produc-

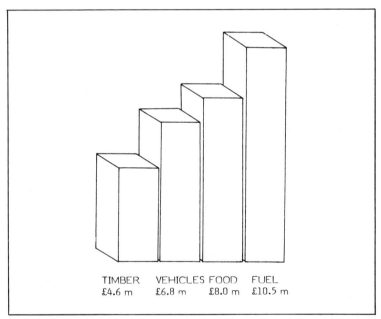

| TIMBER | VEHICLES | FOOD | FUEL |
| £4.6 m | £6.8 m | £8.0 m | £10.5 m |

Figure 12.2 *The cost of timber imports compared to other goods*
Source: British Forestry (Forestry Commission 1986d)

tion, and the stance of the forestry lobby is becoming increasingly isolated.

The volume of timber imports

To avoid the distractions of price, the only accurate way of assessing the trend of timber imports is by their physical volume, or equivalent, in terms of wood raw material equivalent (w.r.m.e.). Figure 12.3 presents a revealing picture. Wood, in the form of sawn timber and roundwood, has never regained its peak level of importation in 1973. Pulp imports have declined steadily since 1970 and panel products have remained stable. Only the consumption of imported paper has steadily increased, as an inevitable consequence of the desire of exporting countries to add value to their products. The total level of all categories of timber imports is shown in Figure 12.4, which also illustrates the slow but steady increase in home timber production. It is clear that rising home production still makes a minor contribution to the overall level of consumption, and a significant proportion of home-grown timber is actually exported.

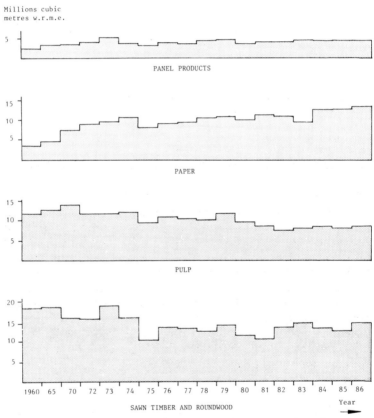

Figure 12.3 *The composition of Britain's timber imports, by volume, in millions of cubic metres w.r.m.e. 1960 to 1986*

Source: Forestry Commission Forestry Facts and Figures

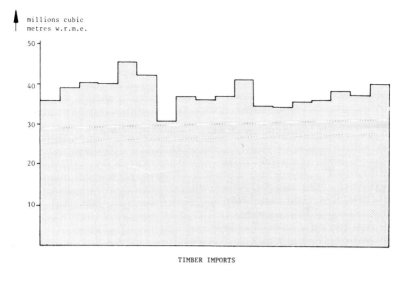

TIMBER IMPORTS

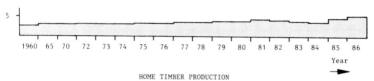

HOME TIMBER PRODUCTION

Figure 12.4 *The total volume of Britain's timber imports, and of home timber production, in millions of cubic metres w.r.m.e. 1960 to 1986*
Source: Forestry Commission Forestry Facts and Figures

The forestry lobby has been fond of making extravagant forecasts of the likely future demand for timber in Britain. *The Wood Production Outlook: a Review* published by the FC in 1977, and the CAS report in 1980, both foresaw massive increases in demand. It always takes a long time for such hopeful predictions, cast far into the future, to be proved wrong, and in the meantime the lobbyists can have a field day with their unsubstantiated claims. But now reality is closing in on the forecasters.

Perhaps the lobby should have been warned by the failure of the FC (1969) to predict the future. The FC foresaw a total timber consumption in Britain in 1980 of 60 million cubic metres w.r.m.e. It was actually only 36.3 million, so that an overestimation of 65 per cent was made in just eleven years.

The FC also failed to predict the wood consumption of the UK, just eight years after the appearance of their 1977 publication. The lowest band of this forecast predicted a consumption of 51 million cubic metres w.r.m.e. for the year 1985, which exceeded reality by

30 per cent. The CAS study can already be seen to be wildly out in its claims. The report estimated that the 1978 UK consumption was 39.4 million cubic metres w.r.m.e. By 1985 it was forecast to rise to 46.0 million, reaching 55.0 million by 2000 and 75.0 million by 2025. The actual figure for consumption in 1985 was only 39.9 million cubic metres w.r.m.e., hardly more than in 1978.

World timber shortages – fact or fiction?

Predictions of world timber shortages are avidly adopted by forestry lobbyists, and feature prominently in the brochures of afforestation companies. But the issues are complex, and widely divergent views are held by some members of Britain's imported timber trade. Robin Howard, for example, said that doomladen documents such as the CAS report were nothing new:

'Those of us with long memories are consoled by the fact that 30 years ago similar reports were being produced which, had they proved accurate, would have us at present in the middle of a worldwide wood famine . . . Every country with an extensive forest industry recognises the need to replant and there are forest reserves and man-made plantations to satisfy any foreseeable demand' (*F & BT* April 1980).

An intensive study of *European Timber Trends and Prospects to the Year 2000 and Beyond* (United Nations 1986) foresaw only moderate growth in consumption and no shortage of wood on international markets around 2000, and suggested that this might raise doubts about the forestry policies of some countries. Looking ahead, the report attached a refreshing importance to the need to develop forests that will offer more flexibility of future supplies and contribute more to multiple-use management.

Forecasts of world timber shortages owe much to the clearance of tropical and sub-tropical forests, for fuelwood and for the creation of agricultural land. Although these pressures are not directly related to British timber imports, useful propaganda can be generated, and is widely used in forestry brochures. A message was delivered to Mrs Thatcher at the British Association which linked the two separate land-use issues and attempted to harness concern about the exploitation of tropical forests to the forestry lobby's own ends:

'You have at last given UK foresters a positive forestry policy which recognises the need for much greater self-sufficiency and an import bill for timber and wood products approaching the enormous sum of £3,000 million per annum . . . natural forests are being destroyed at the rate of an area the size of Wales every seven weeks . . . half of the world's population still depend on wood with which to cook food' (*F & BT* October 1981).

Philip Stewart (1985), himself a member of the team that was responsible for the CAS report, has since disavowed its assumptions and conclusions. He argues that any predicted shortfall of timber in 2030 could be met by tropical plantations, which can grow at least five times as fast as British forests, even if established as late as the year 2020.

Rising timber prices – myth or reality?

The CAS report predicted very substantial rises in timber prices as the theoretical world shortage of timber developed. The economic consultants PIEDA (1986) included the CAS study in a review of nine analyses of future demand/supply trends. Considerable variations were found amongst the studies. The CAS conclusions were regarded as being somewhat extreme, and provided such a range of possible outcomes as to cast considerable doubt on the methodology employed.

In the face of the variety of studies, PIEDA went back to first principles to point out that there is no known instance of significant annual increases in the real price of a basic commodity over several decades. This is explained by the ability of timber users to adopt substitutes, so that timber producers are very restricted in their ability to raise prices. At present, softwood prices are about 90 per cent above the level of 1900, but virtually all of this increase took place during the Second World War. Since 1950 prices have shown no sustained tendency to rise. In this light, PIEDA thought price increases at the top end of the CAS range 'would be a highly unusual outcome, which is almost without parallel in the price of any major basic commodity'.

The FC itself took a sensible view in *The Wood Production Outlook: a Review* (1977), and predicted that timber prices would remain broadly constant to 2025. The forestry companies, however, often include small, but significant price increases in their calculations of prospective financial yield. Small percentage increases of 1 to 2 per cent may sound insignificant, but the cumulative effect is striking. The hopeful predictions of 100 per cent increases on the real price of timber by the year 2025, put forward by the CAS, would come true if annual price increases of about 1.5 per cent took place from 1980.

Grove (1983) also disputes the theory of rising timber prices. He points out that oil reserves, other energy sources, and important metals, may become greatly depleted in the next century, and it should not be readily assumed that timber prices will rise in relation to them.

The most telling point about wishful speculation on timber price rises is made by PIEDA (1986). Any benefit from increased timber prices, in the case of upland conifers, only arises at the end of a long crop rotation of 35 to 45 years. When the rate of return on the overall investment is calculated, the income has to be discounted back over all those years. Even if timber did go up in price by 50 to 150 per cent by 2025, PIEDA calculate that the internal rate of return, achieved by the FC's own planting models, would only increase by 1 to 2.3 per cent. This means that even if timber prices went up by the very large amount of 50 per cent, much of the FC's planting in the north of Scotland would still not even reach the target return of 3 per cent. And some FC planting wouldn't even reach that target if timber prices rose by 150 per cent.

The economics of import saving

The import saving argument for continued afforestation relies on forecasting Britain's world trading position in the year 2025 and beyond, for it is only then that timber from current British afforestation will make a full contribution to reducing imports. The cost of imports at that distant date will be affected by the world price for timber, determined by supply and demand, and the exchange rate which reflects the health of Britain's economy and the balance between total imports and exports.

Obviously, Britain can never produce enough timber to affect the world price, so it is the exchange rate that is most important. Conventional economic wisdom puts forward the key principle of comparative advantage, which is the very foundation of the increased affluence of industrialised nations due to the benefits of world trade. Nations should invest in what they can produce most economically and competitively, and use their earnings from the sale of such goods to buy the imports they need, at the best price, on the world market. Japan, for example, imports more timber and timber products than Britain, and relies on its strong economy to purchase those imports. Japan also has 68 per cent of its land under forest, which is the same proportion as Sweden. Comparative advantage suggests that nations should not direct their investment into uneconomic, lame-duck industries for the sake of saving imports, but into successful enterprises that can compete in world markets. Such a philosophy would seem to be a cornerstone of the Conservative government in 1988, yet the forestry lobby is still influential enough to maintain public investment in poor quality, loss-making, upland conifer afforestation to save imports.

The FC (1977) has acknowledged the principle of comparative advantage:

'It is by no means clear that import saving has any special merit. Participation in international trade gives the opportunity for a country to achieve an overall higher level of economic welfare by allowing production resources to be concentrated in activities to which the country is best suited. The resulting output can then be traded for goods which can be produced more cheaply in other countries.'

The 1972 Treasury Review exploded the myth of import saving, even before it was adopted as government policy, realising that 'there is no value in import saving as such . . .' The Review went on to say that a policy of saving imports 'would be likely to produce only ephemeral success and would also be incompatible with the general aim of reducing trade barriers which has been adopted by successive UK governments'. This was confirmed by the NAO (1986) which found no evidence that the conclusions of the Treasury Review had become invalid: 'In general there appeared to the NAO to be no reason to attach any significant economic value to balance of payments considerations.'

Britain's timber exports

Britain's pulp milling industry was subjected to a devastating slump during the 1970s culminating in the closures of St Annes Boardmill, Wiggins-Teape at Fort William and Bowaters at Ellesmere Port in 1980. In only eight months over 500,000 tonnes of processing capacity for small conifer roundwood was lost. The crisis was rapidly solved, however, by exporting timber to Scandinavia. Figure 12.5 shows that exports peaked rapidly after the mill closures, and declined as alternative home markets were developed. Despite this, timber exports have remained obstinately high since 1984.

The export of highly-subsidised British timber to Scandinavia for processing clearly posed an embarrassing public relations difficulty for the forestry lobby. One of its most enjoyable attempts at saving face was to claim: 'The initiative displayed in creating this trade – hopefully a short term expedient – deserves the highest praise. It keeps our forest workers busy and creates employment and new life in Britain's smaller ports' (*F & BT* February 1981). Later in the year, the export trade was being described as 'fantastically successful' (*F & BT* August 1981). The FC also plays the game,

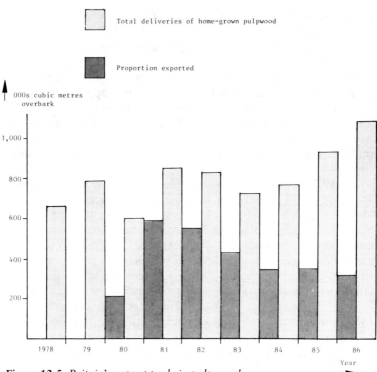

Figure 12.5 *Britain's export trade in pulpwood*
Source: Forestry Commission Forestry Facts and Figures (FC 1987a)

stating that Sitka spruce 'the super tree' is particularly well suited
for paper making: 'As a measure of its popularity for this purpose it
was exported for use in Scandinavian mills following the closure of
three British pulp mills, during the recession in the early 1980s'
(FC undated a).

It is likely that pulpwood exports will continue into the future,
not least because it may not be possible to do anything else with
some of the timber harvested from afforestation in the most remote
and inaccessible parts of Scotland.

Britain's forest industries

As timber begins to be produced from the blanket afforestation
programmes that have been carried out since the Second World
War, there will be a steady, continuing rise in the amount of timber
produced. Since the difficulties of the 1970s, British timber processing investment has concentrated on smaller-scale pulping and on
the production of wood based panels. The backbone of the industry

is currently formed by five integrated pulp/paper mills, six panel plants and 50 major sawmills.

The newly-found 'success' created by the investment in new processing has been very welcome to the forestry lobby. In an attempt to recover from the detailed criticism of the NAO, the lobby is concentrating its propaganda effort on extolling the virtues of forestry as a unified industry. In this way it hopes to downgrade the prominence of unpopular blanket afforestation, and justify it as part of a forestry-industrial complex:

'It is only when these two sides of the industry are seen together – the land-use and the industrial sector – that a true appreciation of the benefits of a national timber resource can be seen; in terms of import substitution, adding value at home rather than abroad . . .' (FICGB News Release 27 March 1987).

Another example of the use of the processing industry to justify yet more afforestation was provided by Fountain Forestry: 'If there are to be more new wood processing industries in Scotland – and there certainly has to be – the current level of new afforestation (which is still not meeting government targets) has to be increased to provide future industrial resources' (*F & BT* March 1987).

Independent economic studies, however, seem to remain impervious to the forestry lobby's enthusiasm about the benefits of the UK's timber industry. PIEDA (1986) think that increased processing by the major timber-growing countries will inevitably tend to shift the UK's imports towards finished goods; but that this will not necessarily raise the price of timber itself, it being more likely that UK processing itself will become uncompetitive. The consultants go on to point out that the price paid for timber by UK industries themselves implies very low returns to new forestry investment. The timber processing industry does not seem to be so abnormally profitable that subsidies to cover afforestation can be justified.

PIEDA also point out that new investment in timber processing usually depends on public sector subsidies, and that four recent, major projects received grants ranging from 18 to 33 per cent. The 1978 expansion at Thames Boardmill by Unilever attracted £28.5 million in government grants out of a total investment of £83 million (*F & BT* June/July 1978). Caberboard's £5 million expansion plans at Cowie stood to receive £1 million of government aid (*F & BT* March 1980), and the new pulp and newsprint mill at Shotton could have qualified for 22 per cent grants from the UK and EEC (*F & BT* August 1982). It should also be remembered that the fortunes of the processing industries over the next 40 years depend on trees that have already been planted. Current planting, much of which will not produce timber from thinnings, will not significantly affect timber supply over that period. This led PIEDA to conclude 'wood processing raises no special issues for the appraisal of current forestry investment'.

Employment in forestry – the bitter debate

Not content with turning one full circle, the cycle of justifications for continued afforestation seems to be beginning another turn. Recent statements from the government and the FC indicate that the principal aims of the WGS are 'to increase timber production and to promote the contribution which new woodlands can make to rural employment . . .' (FC 1988). Other objectives include the provision of an alternative land-use to agriculture, but import-saving is conspicuously absent from the list.

The whole question of assessing the contribution which forestry makes, and ought to make, to rural employment is complicated by the long time-scales involved, and the difficulties of making comparisons with other industries such as agriculture. The situation is not eased by the extravagant claims repeatedly made by forestry lobbyists, and the debate became particularly acrimonious over afforestation in the Flow Country. The NCC's call for a two year, temporary halt to afforestation, in order to weigh up the issues, was greeted by intense reaction from the forestry lobby. The HIDB put out a press release that 2,000 jobs were threatened. This figure, from a dim and distant future, is 55 per cent of the total current industrial labour force of the FC. The HIDB also saw an immediate threat to the 40 full-time and 150 part-time jobs claimed to be provided by Fountain Forestry (*F & BT* January 1987). Conservationists, however, have calculated the entire afforestation programme in the Flow Country could have been carried out by 59 to 74 employees.

The reality of forestry employment

What is certain is that job creation in forestry takes a long time, and there is very little immediate benefit. PIEDA (1986) produced an employment profile, based on figures provided by the FC, for a typical non-thinned crop of Sitka spruce growing on poor peat in the west of Scotland. It was found that each 250 acres (100 ha) of plantation required a labour input of about 60 man years over a 40 year crop rotation. Most importantly, 94 per cent of the employment was generated in the last six years of the life of the crop, and only 3.2 per cent in the first six years. The situation is only improved if a crop can be thinned out after 20 years, but that has become unusual in Scottish blanket afforestation. Stewart (1987) reports an unpublished paper by Laxton and Whitby that if a tree crop is thinned, 40 per cent of total labour requirements are expended on this work.

Mather and Murray (1986) found that in Scottish schemes, one man-year of employment is provided, over each of the first five years, per 494 acres (200 ha) of private afforestation. This can be compared to PIEDA's assessment of the average employment provided by the establishment of the same area of FC plantations, over a six-year period, of 0.65 man-years per year. The gross cost of establishing 494 acres of plantation is close to £200,000, so it is abundantly clear that forestry is no cheap way of providing employment. Neither is it labour intensive. Most of the establishment costs go towards ploughing, fence materials, and the purchase of plants and fertiliser. The labour element is only a small proportion of the total costs, and one man can plant 1–3 acres (0.6–1.2 ha) of land per day, depending on site conditions.

The cyclical nature of forestry work, concentrated at the end of the rotation, and, to a lesser extent, when the trees are first planted, results in a transient, migratory workforce. This is in marked contrast to the typical family workforce, living on a hill farm. Mather and Murray (1986) found that in 57 per cent of their sample schemes the distance travelled was less than 30 miles (50 km), but in 14 per cent of cases it was in excess of 60 miles (100 km). These distances are related to the home bases of firms of contractors, and not to the places of residence of individual workers, which may be even more distant.

In the past, forestry work on landed estates was largely carried out by a resident staff of forestry workers. Mather and Murray (1986) found this pattern no longer exists. Estate staff provided the whole of the labour input in only 5 per cent of the sample cases studied, and part of the input in only a further 10 per cent. The rest of the labour supply came from contractors or the staff of forestry management companies. It is difficult to distinguish between these two categories, because some of the forestry companies use self-employed contractors on a full time basis. Overall, they accounted for the entire labour input on 85 per cent of Scottish private afforestation schemes, and for part of the input on a further 10 per cent of schemes.

Perversely, the forestry lobby even uses the cyclical nature of forestry work as a justification for continued afforestation, simply to maintain employment of the existing gangs of planting workers. Once afforestation begins in a region, the lobby then has a ready-made excuse to plead for it to continue, and this is exactly the tactic that was used in the Flow Country. The lobby also argues that the rate of planting must be maintained to create a balanced range of age classes in the plantations, so that a steady future supply of timber is obtained. This gambit is easily discredited. If large tracts of plantation are reaching the age of felling at about the same time, it is easy to fell some sooner, and some later than their optimum, theoretical rotation length. This process of restructuring allows timber production and labour requirements to be spread more evenly.

The decline in forestry employment

A fatal flaw in the forestry lobby's contention that jobs are created is the actual decline in forestry employment, despite greatly increased planting programmes. The FC itself provides a prime example. After establishing nearly 3,000 sq miles (7,800 sq km) of planting, the number of forest workers employed by the FC today is hardly more than it was in 1935 (FC Annual Reports 1920–84), and is clearly illustrated in Figure 12.6. A small element in this decline is due to use of contractors, especially for harvesting, but the real causes are increasing mechanisation and the reduction in planting programmes (NAO 1986).

Borders Regional Council (1986 a) have also highlighted the failure of afforestation to provide sustained employment. Between 1947 and 1980 the woodland area of the region almost trebled, reaching 167,800 acres (67,931 ha). Despite this vast increase, caused by blanket conifer planting, employment in forestry throughout the Borders actually declined from 614 in 1971 to 440 in 1985. The planners saw no likelihood of a large increase in future employment because of the mechanisation of harvesting operations and increased productivity. Blanket afforestation also appears to have done nothing to halt a 46 per cent decline in the population of the four parishes of Ettrick Forest in the Borders, despite the loss of more than a quarter of the rough grazing on 25,000 acres (10,000 ha) of land (Borders Regional Council 1986 b).

Jobs in timber harvesting are not particularly pleasant, involving heavy manual labour with noisy and potentially dangerous machinery, nor are they well paid. It is not surprising that the TGUK reported that: 'Getting and keeping skilled operators in the private sector is cited as a growing problem in the harvesting sector and has encouraged further investment into mechanised harvesting equipment' (*F & BT* November 1987). There is a clear trend towards massive harvesting machinery, such as timber processors, which can turn out as much timber as 40 men with chainsaws.

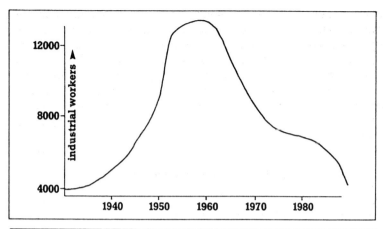

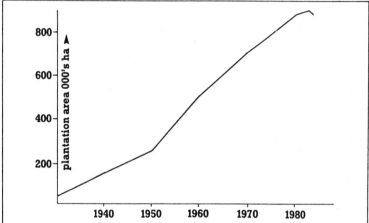

Figure 12.6 *The decline in employment of Forestry Commission forest workers, despite the increasing area of plantation, 1930 to 1985*
Source: Forestry Commission Annual Reports 1929–86

Independent views of forestry employment

Independent assessments of the contribution of forestry to employment are less enthusiastic than those of the forestry lobby. The 1972 Treasury Review concluded that: 'Given the very high implied costs per job in both resource and Exchequer terms, it would appear doubtful whether more effective forms of supporting employment cannot be found nor indeed whether this degree of support is equitable to other areas of long-term unemployment.'

PIEDA (1986) came to the similar conclusion: 'That on any reasonable assumptions, forestry represents a highly expensive mechanism for job creation. Agriculture and other forms of development are significantly less costly *and* provide employment in the near rather than the distant future.'

Subsidies to forestry used to be seen as a way to create employment in deprived rural areas, but the pattern of unemployment appears to have been reversed. PIEDA (1986) reports that over the period 1971–81 trends in total and manufacturing employment were more favourable in rural than urban areas, and that employment in rural Scotland rose by about 80,000 over the ten year period. At precisely the same time, employment in forestry has actually declined. Rural unemployment in Scotland, at around 13 per cent, can be contrasted with unemployment rates of 30 to 40 per cent in the disadvantaged areas of many cities. Clearly, special concessions to employment creation in forestry can no longer be justified.

There is also no reason why the intensified exploitation of hill land, through afforestation, should form the basis of attempts to increase rural employment. PIEDA (1986) made the point that:

'It is sometimes suggested that the costs of job creation in forestry need only be compared with job creation in farming (especially hill farming). This argument rests on the fact that forestry and hill farming are the only two activities which can provide extensive land-use over many of the upland areas of Britain. However, such an approach would confuse the objective of promoting land-use with the objective of creating employment. Even in remote areas, the population is not spread evenly over the countryside and job creation in the main settlements may involve tourism, fisheries or even industrial projects.'

Forestry's hidden subsidies

For 36 years the massive proportion of the costs of blanket afforestation that was met by tax avoidance was kept discreetly veiled by the forestry lobby. A similar level of subsidy is now provided by the FC grants which cover more than 60 per cent of the costs of large blocks of conifer planting, but this is only the tip of the afforestation industry's hidden iceberg of subsidies.

Much of the FC's Forestry Authority role is of direct benefit to private afforestation, and forms an indirect means of subsidisation. The FC also undertakes a very large research programme, which cost nearly £6.6 million during 1986/87. The results of this research are of direct benefit to private forestry interests and are made freely available to them.

Another hidden subsidy to afforestation that has only just emerged is the cost of maintaining and upgrading the rural road network, to take the steadily increasing stream of timber lorries that are forced to use some of the narrowest, and least suitable roads for such traffic. Scotland's Dumfries and Galloway Region estimated that £13 million needed to be spent over eight years, just to keep minor roads up to standard. Borders Region identified more than £6 million of urgent work, and Grampian and Highland Regions foresaw £3.5 million and £2.0 million of expenditure on road maintenance, to combat problems caused by timber lorries (*Scotsman* 8 June 1987). These problems led Dumfries and Galloway to take legal action to recover the cost of repairing a minor road, in a region where 23 per cent of the land is under trees. However, the Secretary of State for Scotland ruled that road damage by timber lorries would have to be funded out of normal capital programmes.

Farming subsidies compared

The forestry lobby is adept at presenting its highly-subsidised industry in the most favourable light. The current debate about agricultural surpluses is used in this way, with the forestry lobby making a direct comparison between agricultural supports costing £2,500 million per year, and forestry tax relief and grants costing only £15 million. This ignores the fact that where afforestation replaces upland sheep farming, a massive increase in subsidisation per unit area of land occurs, which is made plain by the inflation of the land value.

For example, grants to afforest a block of 500 acres (200 ha) of poor quality land amount to £123,000. This sum dwarfs the subsidy of £1,200 per year needed to keep 100 ewes on the land. Afforestation does not replace farming subsidies when part of a farm is planted; it is an additional and costly burden on public expenditure on land that was previously managed at low intensity and with comparatively little financial support.

Recreation

It takes a forestry lobbyist to see the irresistible recreational potential of a dense, dark, unthinned plantation of Sitka spruce. The FC is proud of the commercial success of its holiday cabins and campsites, which are far more profitable than growing Sitka spruce, and makes much of these recreational facilities in its campaigning role in the forestry lobby.

Figure 12.7 *Anyone for a picnic? This gloomy prospect is hardly appetising*

Overall, the FC has eight forest drives, 17 visitor centres, 33 camping and caravan sites, 192 forest cabins and holiday houses, 624 picnic places, and 646 forest walks and nature trails (1986 d). The figures are superficially impressive, until it is remembered that the FC has almost 2.2 million acres (890,000 ha) of land under plantations in Britain. Thus there is one camp-site for every 66,000 acres (27,000 ha) of plantation, and one forest walk and picnic place for every 3,500 acres (1,400 ha) of tree crops. Given current establishment costs of £400 per acre (£1,000 per ha), that is one forest walk per £1.4 million of public expenditure. It would be surprising if cheaper ways of creating more attractive recreational opportunities could not be found.

PIEDA (1986) found that FC forests under 25 years of age are of little recreational benefit, especially those in remote areas where most afforestation is taking place. The consultants also pointed out that 'most recreational use of forests takes place within a very short distance of roads or access points . . .' This is hardly surprising in view of the hostile, prickly thicket of trees that prevents anything more than superficial access. It is abundantly clear there is no need to plant 3,500 acres (1,400 ha) of land to create a single forest walk.

The private sector of the forestry lobby is generally wary of public recreation and abysmally poor at providing recreational opportunities. The FC seems reluctant to admit this, or even to encourage improvements. Mather and Murray (1986) found no provision for outdoor recreation was made in 85 per cent of the sample of private Scottish afforestation schemes that they studied. Informal use for activities such as pony trekking was permitted by forest managers in around 10 per cent of their sample, and formal arrangements (usually for shooting by people other than the owners) were reported from 5 per cent. Mather and Murray concluded that recreation in private forests 'may be discouraged, if not prevented, by notices or electric fences, even if access stiles are provided. The general impression often conveyed at the access points is that recreationists are not positively welcomed.'

Such findings are confirmed by the Borders Regional Council (1986 a):

'Few planting schemes carried out by private forest companies include any recreational provision and it is considered that the Regional Council should make representations to the Forestry Commission asking that private forestry companies include recreation provision in any large Forestry Grant Scheme and existing schemes should be examined in order to determine new recreational opportunities.'

Despite the paucity of recreation provision by the FC, and the general absence of facilities in private forests, the forestry lobby still uses the supposed recreational value of forests to support its expansionist claims: 'If a significant weakening of support for Britain's forestry industry were to take place on the basis of the NAO review it would have important implications for a number of other policy areas, including . . . recreation and tourism' (Firn, Crichton and Roberts Ltd 1987).

= 13 =

An Agenda for the Future

The way ahead

It is time for forestry policy to be rethought, revitalised and modernised, to take account of the ever-increasing complexity of forestry and woodland management. The closure of the tax-avoidance loophole offers an opportunity to create a new approach to forestry, and it is one that must not be missed by conservation and environmental concerns. It is possible that the forestry lobby will be receptive to some of the necessary reforms, and vulnerable to the logic of others, at the present time.

There are dangers if the opportunity is missed, and temptations which mean that it might be. Forestry's 'big bang' may well result in a lull in upland afforestation programmes, and it would be easy for the advocates of reform to relax their efforts. They should be warned that any reduction in planting levels is only likely to be a temporary phenomenon and that the forestry lobby, which even now is actively and publicly campaigning, has survived similar crises in the past. A new market in forestry land will soon be created, and the forestry lobby will continue to call for increased incentives to speed its development. Tax avoidance may have ceased, but the structure, rationale and profit-base of the forestry-industrial complex remains rooted in blanket, conifer afforestation.

The first step on the road to change must be for the whole range of environmental and countryside groups that are concerned with forestry policy to follow the example that the forestry lobby itself has set, and join forces, to agree a unified approach to forestry reform. The constituency of such groups would be so large, and could represent organisations with over 700,000 members, that this alone would make it difficult for government to ignore or sidetrack its recommendations. A thorough review of forestry policy would be undertaken, and guidelines produced for the restructuring of the forestry establishment.

During the five year transitional period after the 'big bang', tax avoidance will still be available to existing forest owners. This will allow an expansion of upland forestry schemes by owners who had planned to stage their planting over several years, as is often the

176

case, and will mean that owners of some traditional wooded estates can continue to draw on Schedule D support for their woodland management. It is very important that the pattern of new planting is carefully monitored during this period, to find out who is planting, under what incentives, and what the location, extent and nature of their operations are.

New objectives

An immediate and crucial reform must be the abandonment of a target area of afforestation which, in practice, applies almost solely to upland planting. This is an obsolete concept that took root 70 years ago, and has completely outlived its purpose. The continuance of it is solely due to the propagandising of the forestry lobby, and is a sure indication of the fact that the only really profitable activity of the afforestation industry, under existing incentives, is blanket planting contracts. Once the obsession with a target which can only be met by planting hill land is abolished, then import saving can be jettisoned as the basis for forestry expansion, because it was only ever adopted to justify having a target in the first place.

The FWS should form the basis of any expansion of tree planting. It has the potential to encourage a wider range of tree species to be planted, in smaller units, on more fertile land. The FWS is intended to avoid planting on semi-natural habitats that have an existing conservation value, and to allow afforestation of improved farm-land that has already lost much of its conservation interest. Although such planting cannot be judged as economic by normal criteria, it can be justified to reduce agricultural surpluses. The FWS is seen as a possible threat by the forestry lobby which is anxious that it does not result in a diversion of subsidies and targets away from the uplands. There is scope for environmental organisations to expose the vulnerability of the forestry lobby on this issue.

The basis for the future of forestry must be founded on the maintenance and management of a varied woodland resource that can provide the maximum range of benefits to the nation. This would involve full recognition of the value of small-scale, broad-leaved woodlands for landscape and wildlife. Such a woodland heritage is far more likely to be valued by future generations, and forestry policy needs to be steered towards the encouragement of sound management, rather than a preoccupation with upland planting targets, in order to achieve it.

Timber production should, of course, continue to be a vital objective in many woodlands, and a dominant one in the upland conifer plantations that would continue to supply the existing wood processing industries. Timber production would continue to be recognised as an objective of growing broadleaves in smaller woodlands, but not always the priority. Sound woodland management would create employment, but this would not be a justification in itself.

New incentives

Both incentives and controls are needed to implement a proper forestry policy. Incentives are required because timber production in Britain has never been able to provide a sound economic basis to sustain forestry in its own right. Incentives to woodland owners are also justified when trees provide benefits to the rest of the population, and these benefits can be passed down to future generations. However, it is not possible to design incentives so precisely that they achieve only the desired results. The lessons from the abuse of tax avoidance as a forestry incentive took a long time to learn, and proper controls and monitoring are an essential counterpart to the provision of incentives. This is particularly important when such a large investment of public money is being made.

Some tuning of the existing planting grants is clearly needed. It is beyond argument that the nature of current, large-scale, conifer afforestation schemes cause environmental problems. A tapering of the grant bands would help to discourage large schemes, and end the iniquity of a single rate of planting grant for any scheme larger than 25 acres (10 ha). In future, the per acre rate of planting grant should be gradually, and progressively reduced as planting schemes increase in size from 25–50 acres (10–20 ha), 50–100 acres (20–40 ha), and 100–200 acres (40–80 ha). Any larger afforestation schemes would only be eligible for grant aid on the first 200 acres (80 ha) of planting that they contained. The revised planting grants would confirm that there was still scope for extensive planting schemes in some parts of the countryside, but new planting in the uplands would cease to be the dominant theme of forestry policy.

An essential feature of forestry management is long-term planning, which must necessarily span human generations. This should be encouraged by a return to the keeping of more detailed management plans and records as a condition of grant aid.

Annual management grants should certainly be provided as part of a shift back towards the renewed emphasis on woodland management for multiple objectives. This would also be supported by the TGUK, as so many of their members will lose the incentives of

Schedule D tax avoidance, which played an important but less conspicuous role in supporting the management of existing woodlands, particularly on traditional estates. Management grants would restore these incentives on a more equitable basis and could apply to all woodland owners, whatever their circumstances. These grants should also be tapered in line with planting grants, so that small woodlands with their dis-economies of scale, would receive appropriate incentives. Management grants would be available for woodlands over 200 acres (80 ha) in extent, but at reduced levels, and would also differentiate between coniferous and broadleaved woodlands.

New controls

There is an urgent need for controls on the quality of any land that is afforested in the uplands in the future, in order to avoid the tendency of subsidies to encourage the planting of poor quality land. The system of windthrow hazard classification developed by the FC (see Chapter 10) provides a convenient basis to achieve this.

From now on, no land of WHC 5 or 6 should be afforested, even though it may already have been approved for planting. This would ensure that almost all plantations established in future years could be properly thinned. Such plantations not only provide a higher return on the initial investment, but are more likely to be of value in terms of wildlife interest and recreation, and provide more employment than unthinned plantations. The new guidelines would drastically curtail further afforestation of contentious sites in Scotland, such as the Flow Country and other remote, poor-quality sites.

In other areas the guidelines would help to prevent afforestation from expanding into such huge blocks and from extending too far up hillsides. New planting would be restricted to better areas of soils on the lower ground. It was on such land that tree planting tended to take place in the past, mainly before the Second World War. It is common experience to see well-sited woodlands on the lower slopes of hill land in Scotland, with the ploughlines of modern, blanket afforestation extending across large areas of less suitable land above them. It is likely that restricting new planting to land in WHC 1–4 would do a great deal to reduce such problems, although further controls would still be necessary in order to prevent the excessive afforestation of semi-natural habitats on some areas of WHC 4 land.

Planning control should also be belatedly extended to cover all afforestation schemes over 25 acres (10 ha). This would permit the democratic and public scrutiny of the entrustment of a large public investment to private interests. As an essential background to their decision-making process, and to end the piecemeal, haphazard approach to land-use planning, local authorities should be responsible for zoning their upland countryside into three zones. Heritage zones would be created, embracing all existing designated areas, where the aim would be to conserve and enhance existing landscape and wildlife values. Substantial new heritage zones would need to be established throughout Scotland to protect the best examples of the variety of hills and moorland. Intermediate, conservation zones would also be drawn where a mixed system of land-use would be developed, with guidelines on the balance to be achieved. Finally, there would be zones where forestry could continue to be the dominant land-use through a wider extension of new planting. An essential part of the process of zoning would be the revelation of the secret land bank, so that it could be clearly seen just what land the FC has already approved for blanket afforestation.

If a forestry application was not agreed by the planning authority, then it would be open for the applicant to pursue the matter through the normal system of planning appeals. Planting schemes of less than 25 acres (10 ha) would not need full planning approval, but would still be subject to the system of voluntary consultation that exists at present. From past experience it seems that little objection would be made to most such smaller planting schemes. If agreement could not be reached during the consultation process, these smaller planting schemes would also be passed into the planning system. There would be no future place for the RACs in land-use decisions, and they would be disbanded.

A new forestry service

A crucial element in forestry reform must be the splitting of the FC into its separate Authority and Enterprise roles. Freed from the domination of the forestry-industrial complex, the Authority could form the basis of a newly constituted Forestry Service, and could take on what should be the proper, vital role of foresters everywhere – that of the guardians and protectors of all woodlands. This would open the way for the salvation of the forestry profession from its image as the despoiler of the environment, and restore it to what it always should have been. Prince Charles (1988) is clearly aware of the opportunities for reform:

'The United Kingdom seems to be one of the few countries in the world where afforestation is treated with suspicion and sometimes outright opposition. This is hardly surprising when the planting up of heather moorlands and other valued areas with dense Sitka spruce and lodgepole pine takes place on a large scale ... the Forestry Commission's remit is too narrow to allow it to assume the wider social, environmental and heritage role that woods and forests could play in our lives. Only by a fundamental review of the Forestry Commission's remit and of the future role of forestry are we likely to see forests become a part of the natural heritage of this country, as they are in Germany and other European nations; and not simply planted in interminable furrows to be harvested like fields of wheat.'

The new Forestry Service would be staffed by professional foresters, together with specialists such as ecologists and landscape architects, who would be responsible for the administration of grant aid to woodlands, supervision of management planning, and control of the continued system of felling licences. Applications to afforest land would have to meet standards set by the Forestry Service before entering the consultation process or being submitted for planning approval.

An important objective of the Forestry Service would be to fill the gulf left by the withdrawal of the FC from small-scale, lowland forestry and be responsible for the provision of freely available advice to woodland owners. This is a seriously neglected aspect of British forestry, which has become fragmented between a number of different sources. The importance of advice to woodland owners is more widely appreciated in many other countries such as France, West Germany and the Netherlands. Many owners are very keen to manage their woodlands properly and the best forestry advice may be the only catalyst that is needed.

The Forestry Service would be accountable to a Forestry Council which would contain a full representation from all groups with an interest in forestry policy. Representatives from both voluntary and government environmental organisations would be able to play the fullest role, and timber industry representatives and woodland owners would also have their place on the Council. It would, of course, be vital to ensure that the Forestry Council did not become simply another manifestation of the existing FC and careful balancing of interests would need to take place to ensure that it did not become dominated by the camp-followers of the FC.

The Forestry Council would be responsible for approving the upland land-use zones prepared by local authorities and for ensuring that these were in accordance with national policy guidelines. Forestry Service foresters in the field would be guided by such policy and management guidelines, set by the Council after consultation with all interested organisations and individuals.

New woodland owners and managers

The separation of the FC into its twin roles, through the creation of a Forestry Service, would leave the way open for the privatisation of the bulk of the FC's estate of upland, coniferous plantations. The most likely purchasers would be financial institutions, using the forestry companies as their advisers. There are those who would feel uneasy about such a sale, but they should not be misled by the vestiges of the homely, tweed-clad image of the FC. The majority of its upland plantations are nothing more than industrial, cellulose factories, with minimal recreational opportunities, and management by the private sector would be just as appropriate.

Full public access to FC plantations that were sold would be guaranteed and legally ensured. There would be an important role for the Forestry Service to encourage specific provisions for recreation as a condition of future grant aid. The privatisation of FC holdings would, however, not extend to unique sites such as the New Forest and the Forest of Dean. The management of such woodlands could be transferred to the Countryside Commissions or bodies similar to the national park authorities. Other areas of woodland which are important for wildlife and recreation, would either have their ownership and management transferred to local authorities and the NCC, or would be sold at valuation to county naturalists' trusts and other voluntary conservation groups. There would be no open market sale of such vital public assets.

The revenue from the sale of the FC's industrial, conifer plantations would be used to form a British Forestry Trust which would help to finance the operations of the Forestry Service. The real benefit from the splitting of the FC and privatisation of much of the Forestry Enterprise, would be a restoration of full public control over the course of forestry, through a greatly widened and strengthened Forestry Council. The way would be open for the Forestry Service to act as the true guardian of Britain's woodland heritage.

Bibliography

BAGULEY, M. (1985) Forestry – a growing concern. *Landscape Scotland Quarterly 2 No 2*: 11–12

BOND, M. (1988) Flow country reaches a watershed. *Chartered Surveyor Weekly 8 Sept 1988*: 75–77

BORDERS REGIONAL COUNCIL (1986 a) Report by Director of Planning and Development. *Forestry and Woodlands in the Borders Region* Newtown St Boswells

────── (1986 b) *Ettrick Forest Local Plan – Draft*. Newtown St Boswells

BOWERS, J.K. (1983) *The Economics of Upland Land-use*. Leeds University School of Economics

BUCCLEUCH, DUKE OF (1988) In defence of conifers. *Daily Telegraph*, 2 April

CALLANDER, R.F. (1987) *A Pattern of Landownership in Scotland*. Haugh-end Publications, Finzean, Aberdeenshire

CENTRE FOR AGRICULTURAL STRATEGY (1978) *Landownership by Public and Semi-public Institutions in the UK*. Reading

────── (1980) *Strategy for the UK Forest Industry*. Reading

CHARLES, PRINCE OF WALES (1988) Speech quoted in *Scottish Wildlife* Magazine of the SWT. Summer 1988. Edinburgh

CLEGG, J. & CO (1986) *Forestry Review of 1985*. Edinburgh

COUNTRY LANDOWNERS ASSOCIATION (1986) *Forestry and the Landowner: Verney Working Party*. London

COUNTRYSIDE COMMISSION (1984) *A Better Future for the Uplands*. Cheltenham

────── (1987 a) *Forestry in the Countryside CCP 245*. Cheltenham

────── (1987 b) *New Opportunities for the Countryside*. Cheltenham

CROWE, DAME S. (1986) The forest's potential for recreation and landscape. In D. Jenkins (ed.) *Symposium on Trees and Wildlife in the Scottish Uplands*. Institute of Terrestrial Ecology, Abbots Ripton

DAVIES, E.J.M. (1982) The next big one. *Forestry and British Timber 11 No 3*: 24–25

────── (1985) *Forestry in Scotland*. FC, Edinburgh

DEVALL, N. AND BROTHERTON, I. (1986) *Afforestation Consultation in National Parks 1974–84*. Department of Landscape Architecture, University of Sheffield

DOUGLASS, R. (1986) A view of forestry with special reference to Mull. *Scottish Forestry 40 No 2*: 87–106

DRAKEFORD, T. (1979) *Report of Survey of the Afforested Spawning Grounds of the Fleet Catchment*. FC, Dumfries (unpublished report)

────── (1982) *Management of Upland Streams (an Experimental Fisheries*

Management Project on the Afforested Head Waters of the River Fleet, Kirkcudbrightshire. Paper delivered to Institute of Fisheries Management, 12th Annual Study Course, Durham

ECONOMIC FORESTRY GROUP (1984) *EFG Magazine 1984.* Oxford
_____ (1985 a) *Forestry: an Introduction for Investors.* Oxford
_____ (1985 b) *EFG Magazine 1985.* Oxford
_____ (1985 c) *Investment Bulletin No. 2.* Edinburgh
_____ (1986 a) *Private Investment Bulletin.* Edinburgh
_____ (1986 b) *Investment Opportunities in Britain for Pension Funds and Life Assurance Companies.* Edinburgh
_____ (1986 c) *EFG Magazine 1986.* Oxford
_____ (1987) *Private Forestry Investment Review.* London
_____ (undated a) *Eskdalemuir.* Moffat

EGGLISHAW, H., GARDINER, R. AND FOSTER, J. (1986) Salmon catch decline and forestry in Scotland. *Scottish Geographical Magazine 102 No 1:* 57–61

EVANS, H.F. (1984 a) Vigilance is vital in spruce beetle war. *Forestry and British Timber 13 No. 6:* 21–23
_____ (1984 b) Spruce bark beetle: two years after. *EFG Magazine 1984:* 11–12. EFG, Oxford

FIRN, CRICHTON AND ROBERTS LTD (1987) *The Forestry Industry Response to the NAO Report: prepared for the FICGB.* Edinburgh

FORESTRY COMMISSION (1919–1987) *FC Annual Reports* HMSO, London
_____ (1969) *Imports and Consumption of Wood Products in the UK 1950–1967 with Forecasts to 1980.* FC Forest Record No. 70. HMSO, London
_____ (1971) *Windblow of Scottish Forests in January 1968.* Bulletin No. 45. HMSO, London
_____ (1977) *The Wood Production Outlook in Britain: a Review.* Edinburgh
_____ (1979) *Gilpinia hercyniae: a Pest of Spruce.* Forest Record 117. HMSO, London
_____ (1984) *Census of Woodlands and Trees.* Edinburgh
_____ (1985 a) *Windthrow Hazard Classification.* Leaflet 85. HMSO, London
_____ (1985 b) *Guide to Upland Restocking.* Leaflet 84. HMSO, London
_____ (1985 c) *Controls to Prevent the Spread of the Great Spruce Bark Beetle.* Edinburgh
_____ (1986 a) *FC 66th Annual Report and Accounts 1985/86.* HMSO, London
_____ (1986 b) *The Forestry Commission and Conservation.* Policy and Procedure Paper No. 14. Edinburgh
_____ (1986 c) *Kielder Forest Management Plan 1986–90.* Bellingham
_____ (1986 d) *British Forestry: Industry Year 1986.* Edinburgh
_____ (1987 a) *Forestry Facts and Figures.* Edinburgh
_____ (1987 b) *Census of Woodlands and Trees 1979–82.* HMSO, London
_____ (1987 c) *Forest Facts 2 – the FC.* Edinburgh
_____ (1987 d) *FC 67th Annual Report and Accounts 1986/87.* HMSO, London
_____ (1987 e) *Forestry in Caithness and Sutherland: Report for Highland Regional Council Working Party.* Inverness

_____ (1987 f) *Forest Facts 3 – Timber Production in Britain.* Edinburgh
_____ (1988) *Woodland Grant Scheme.* Edinburgh
_____ (undated a) *Sitka Spruce: the Super Tree.* Edinburgh
FORESTRY COMMITTEE OF GREAT BRITAIN (1971) *The Case for Forestry.* London
FORESTRY INDUSTRY COMMITTEE OF GREAT BRITAIN (1987) *Totality of Forestry Not Understood.* News Release, 27 March. London
FOUNTAIN FORESTRY (1986 a) *Forestry Facts: England, Scotland and Wales.* London
_____ (1986 b) *Forestry Investment and Taxation: The Professional's Guide.* London
_____ (1987) *Forestry Investment in North America.* London
GRAYSON, A.J. (1981) Current FC thinking on thinning. *Forestry and British Timber 10 No. 8:* 46–49
_____ (1982) *Broadleaves in Britain.* FC, Alice Holt
GROVE, R. (1983) *The Future for Forestry.* British Association of Nature Conservationists, Cambridge
HANSARD (1986) Forestry Bill. *Hansard HL:* 802, 17 June
_____ (1988 a) Forestry Debate. *Hansard HL* 13 April
_____ (1988 b) Forestry Debate. *Hansard HL* 17 February
HARPER, W. (1986) To thin or not to thin: optimising present and future returns to the grower. *Forestry and British Timber 15 No. 12:* 22–27
HARRIMAN, R. AND MORRISON, B.R.S. (1982) Ecology of streams draining forested and non-forested catchments in an area of central Scotland subject to acid precipitation. *Hydrobiologica 88:* 251–263
HART, C.E (1987) *Private Woodlands: a Guide to British Timber Prices and Forestry Costings.* Coleford, Gloucs
HETHERINGTON, M.J. (1988) Afforestation consultations in Northern Scotland: a case study of the voluntary system in action. *Scottish Forestry 42 No 3:* 185–191
HOLMES, G.D. (1979) An introduction to forestry in upland Britain. In E.D. Ford, D.C. Malcolm and J. Atterson (eds.) *The Ecology of Even-aged Forest Plantations.* Institute of Terrestrial Ecology, Cambridge
HOUSE OF COMMONS, COMMITTEE OF PUBLIC ACCOUNTS (1980) *Eighth Report: Inland Revenue: Taxation.* HMSO, London
HOUSE OF COMMONS, COMMITTEE OF PUBLIC ACCOUNTS (1987) *Twelfth Report: Forestry Commission: Review of Objectives and Achievements.* HMSO, London
INTERNATIONAL MIRE CONSERVATION GROUP (1986) Press Release, 26 September
JANIS, I.L. (1972) *Victims of Group Think.* Houghton Mifflin, Boston
JEFFREY, E.H.W., ASHMOLE, M.A. AND MACRAE, F.M.(1986) The economics of wildlife in private forestry. In D. Jenkins (ed.) *Symposium on Trees and Wildlife in the Scottish Uplands.* Institute of Terrestrial Ecology, Abbots Ripton
KING, C. AND FIELDING, N. (1987) Spruce beetle four years on: *Dendroctonus micans* update. *Forestry and British Timber 16 No. 4:* 21–24
LAXTON, H. AND WHITBY, M. To be published. *Rural Employment: the Effect of Afforestation in the Uplands*
LEATHER, S.R. (1986) Keep an eye out for the vapourer moth. *Forestry and British Timber 15 No. 7:* 13

MATHER, A.S. (1987) The structure of forest ownership in Scotland: a first approximation. *Journal of Rural Studies 3 No. 2*: 175–182

―――― and MURRAY, N.C. (1986) *Private-sector Afforestation in Scotland*. Aberdeen University Geography Department Study Paper 7. Aberdeen

MCEWEN, J. (1981) *Who Owns Scotland*. Polygon, Edinburgh

MILLER, PROF. H. (1985) Letter to the *New Scientist*, 5 December

MONCRIEFF, A. (1985) The investment scene. *EFG Magazine 1985* EFG, Oxford

―――― (1986) The investment scene. *EFG Magazine 1986* EFG, Oxford

MOORE, P.J. (1985) The unacceptable face of private forestry. *Ecos 6 No 4*: 34–40

NATIONAL AUDIT OFFICE (1986) *Review of Forestry Commission Objectives and Achievements*. HMSO, London

NATURE CONSERVANCY COUNCIL (1984) *Nature Conservation in Great Britain*. Peterborough

―――― (1986) *Nature Conservation and Afforestation in Britain*. Peterborough

―――― (1987) *Birds, Bogs and Forestry: The Peatlands of Caithness and Sutherland*. Peterborough

NEWSON, M. (1985) Forestry and water in the uplands of Britain: the background of hydrological research and options for harmonious land-use. *Quarterly Journal of Forestry 79*: 113–120

NORMAN, C. (1980) Observations quoted in Scottish forestry commentary. *Forestry and British Timber 9 No 9*: 10

OGILVY, R.S.D. (1986) Whither forestry? The scene in AD 2025. In D. Jenkins (ed.) *Symposium on Trees and Wildlife in the Scottish Uplands*. Institute of Terrestrial Ecology, Abbots Ripton

PIEDA (1986) *Forestry in Great Britain: An Economic Assessment for the National Audit Office*. Edinburgh

―――― (1988) *Budgeting for British Forestry*. CPRE, London

RATCLIFFE, D.A. (1986) The effects of afforestation on the wildlife habitats of open ground. In D.Jenkins (ed.) *Symposium on Trees and Wildlife in the Scottish Uplands*. Institute of Terrestrial Ecology, Abbots Ripton

ROBINSON, M. AND BLYTH, K. (1982) The effect of forestry drainage operations on upland sediment yields: a case study. *Earth Surface Processes and Landforms 7*: 85–90

ROLLINSON, T. (1985) Windthrow and price are main thinning factors. *Forestry and British Timber 14 No. 10*: 22–24

ROWAN, A.A. (1986) The nature of British upland forests in the 1980s. In D. Jenkins (ed.) *Symposium on Trees and Wildlife in the Scottish Uplands*. Institute of Terrestrial Ecology, Abbots Ripton

ROYAL COMMISSION (1979) *Distribution of Income and Wealth Report No. 7*. Cmnd. 7595. HMSO, London

RSPB (1985) *Forestry in the Flow Country: The Threat to Birds*. Sandy

―――― (1987) *Forestry in the Flows of Caithness and Sutherland*. Sandy

SANDISON, B. (1986) Letter to the *Scotsman*, 3 December

SHOARD, M. (1987) *This Land is Our Land*. Grafton, London

STEWART, P.J. (1985) British forestry policy – time for a change. *Land Use Policy*, January: 16–19

―――― (1987) *Growing Against the Grain: United Kingdom Forestry Policy*. CPRE, London

STROUD, D.A. AND REED, T.M. (1986) The effect of plantation proximity on moorland breeding waders. *Wader Study Group. Bulletin 46*: 25–28

SURVIVAL ANGLIA LTD (1988) 'Paradise Ploughed'. Transcript of television documentary. London

SYSON, W.W.C. (1985) Forestry financing – Scottish bank plays major role. *Forestry and British Timber 14 No 9*: 30–32

TAYLOR, D. (1981) Will pension funds play ball? *Forestry and British Timber 10 No 3*:20–21

——— (1987 a) The forestry debate. *The Farmland Market*, August: 12–13

——— (1987 b) Forest industry must broaden its base. *Forestry and British Timber 16 No 1*: 17–18

——— (1988) Woodland market will ride out the storm. *Forestry and British Timber 17 No 1*: 33–35

TILHILL FORESTRY (1988) *Forestry Investment for Institutions*. Farnham, Surrey

TIMBER GROWERS' ORGANISATION (1972) *Timber Grower*. London

——— (1973) *Twelfth Annual General Meeting: Report of the Council and Statement of Accounts*. London

——— (1978) *Seventeenth Annual General Meeting: Report of the Council and Statement of Accounts*. London

——— (1980) *Timber Grower*. London

TIMBER GROWERS UNITED KINGDOM (1985) *The Forestry and Woodland Code*. London

——— (1986) *Afforestation and Nature Conservation: Interactions*. London

TOMPKINS, S.C. (1986) *The Theft of the Hills: Afforestation in Scotland*. Ramblers Association, London

TREASURY (1972) *Forestry in Great Britain: an Inter-departmental Cost/Benefit Study*. HMSO, London

UNITED NATIONS (1986) *European Timber Trends and Prospects to the Year 2000 and Beyond* (ETTS IV). Reference ECE/Tim/30. United Nations Sales No. E 86.11.E.19

WATSON, J., LANGSLOW, D.R. AND RAE, S.R. (1987) *The Impact of Land-use Changes on Golden Eagles in the Scottish Highlands*. NCC, Peterborough

WILLIAMS, R. (1984) Private sector responds to investment challenge. *EFG Magazine 1984* EFG, Oxford

Index

unproductive woodland 146
uplands
　afforestation 13
　England 3–4, 14
　Scotland 3–5, 14
　Wales 3–4, 14
　zoning 180

water 31
Wildlife and Countryside Act 1981
　111
Wildlife and Countryside
　(Amendment) Bill 1985 97
wind damage 25, 133

windthrow
　catastrophic 124–6
　endemic 126–7
　hazard classification (WHC)
　　127–8, 129, 179
*Wood Production Outlook: a
　Review* 12, 113, 161–2
Woodland Grant Scheme (WGS)
　44, 57, 70–1, 73, 146, 151, 168
world trade 164

yield class 131–2

Zuckerman Committee 11